C000053583

WILD FLOWERS

OF THE

NORTH YORK MOORS
NATIONAL PARK

by Sylvia M. Arnold

Photographs by
John M. Arnold

HUTTON PRESS
1986

Copyright © 1986
The Hutton Press Limited
130 Canada Drive, Cherry Burton, Beverley
East Yorkshire HU17 7SB

ISBN 0 907033 42 3

Phototypeset in 11 on 12 point Times Roman
and Printed by
The Walkergate Press Limited
Lewis House, Springfield Way, Anlaby, Hull HU10 6RX

DEDICATION

In Memory of my Father, Arthur Old,
for a lifetime of encouragement
and the gift of confidence.

ACKNOWLEDGEMENTS

I am indebted to Nan Sykes for discussions about the content of this book and to Hilary Fowler, Fred Garrett and members of my wild flower classes for records taken during my field trips and for continuing discussions about local habitats.
I would also like to thank Sonia Donaghy for her help in the preparation of the manuscript.
The Publisher wishes to thank Mr. D. C. Statham, the North York Moors National Park Officer, for permission to reproduce the map of the Park at the beginning of the text.

Sylvia Arnold
July 1986

LIST OF CONTENTS

Front cover: Marsh Marigolds *(Caltha palustris)* along the Derwent in the Forge Valley National Nature Reserve.

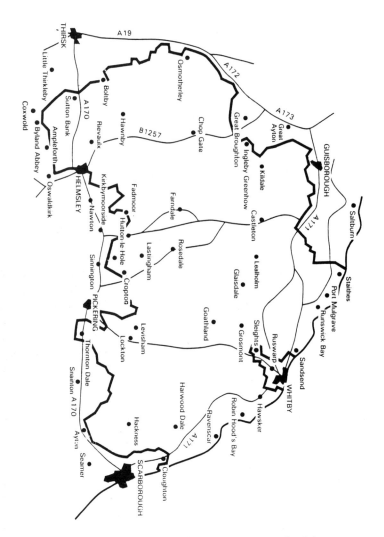

The North York Moors National Park encompasses much of the eastern part of the county of North Yorkshire, lying between the coastal resorts of Scarborough and Whitby in the east and the market towns of Thirsk and Northallerton in the west. The Moors rise northwards from the Vale of Pickering and include the Cleveland Hills and the Hambleton Hills. The Park occupies an area of 553 square miles and includes a number of Yorkshire Wildlife Trust Reserves, the National Nature Reserve at Forge Valley and Gormire Lake, one of only three natural lakes in Yorkshire.

INTRODUCTION

My father and grandmother were great storytellers. As a child I listened to many tales about the North Yorkshire Moors: my grandmother was born at Foss Farm near Littlebeck and when her step-father was kicked by a bull they had to leave their farming tenancy for work in a country pub at Hawsker – a moorland life where winter snows were as high as the hedgerow, long summer days were clear and hot, and autumn hands were stained blue with masses of Bilberries, eaten piping hot in pies with cream. My father told of epic hikes laden with luggage, walks necessary for economy rather than exercise, and many a wide-ranging Home Guard manoeuvre over moor and valley, field and hedgerow, staged on the Moors when the country was at war. From childhood my interests quickly became concentrated on wild flowers and my feet have often turned to these traditional family haunts. My expectations from the Moors were coloured by these technicolour memories but in spite of this the area has never disappointed me. As a naturalist the Moors offer me beautiful scenery, a profusion of wild flowers, tranquil glades disturbed only by tumbling water and the humming bee; or wild, high and windswept one can walk for miles across open countryside crossing from hill to valley, moorland to coastal path.

The landscape I describe is included within the North Yorkshire Moors National Park which covers 553 square miles and offers many different habitats for plant growth: deep shady ravines with cascading waterfalls, open Heather clad moors, dramatic cliffs falling to the foaming sea and quiet verdant valleys approached through winding lanes and dotted with farms. A complex geology and dramatic glacial history combine with man's use of the landscape to create this kaleidoscope. The soils of the Park offer the most extreme contrasts between acid, porous soils derived from sandstone and shallow, calcareous soils weathered from the limestone.

The flowers of this area are beautiful, their story being not of one moment but of centuries of change and development. Their history reflects not only man's occupation and exploitation of the area but goes back beyond the first Neolithic settlements to the cool dawn following the long frozen winter night of the last great Ice Age. Let's wipe the slate clean and begin at the new beginning.

Once upon a time the climate became cold, and great glaciers formed in the mountains of Britain. With so much water tied up in ice flows, sea levels dropped across the world, and Britain was joined to the Continent by the dry sea bed of the English Channel. Huge glaciers flowed south from the Lake District, Teesdale and Scotland. When they reached the high ground of the North Yorkshire Moors the flows bifurcated, the largest flow travelling south down the Vale of York and a second travelling east to Teesside. The North Sea was frozen with ice originating from Scandinavia. The Moors were above the general level of the ice and were covered in thousands of feet of snow. Animals had migrated south or perished and plant life is assumed to have been eliminated.

Ten thousand years ago the climate gradually became milder and the snow on the Moors began to melt. Melt-waters could not drain away easily, their escape being blocked by the great ice flows. Accumulating waters created a large lake along the Esk valley. As temperatures gradually rose, more snow and ice melted and the lake basin filled to overflow along the head of Newtondale. This great valley was scoured out as the main overflow channel for the waters from Lake Esk. Many smaller valleys were cut through the sandstone tableland at this same period. Thus was created the typical moorland landscape of flat moors dropping to narrow steep-sided valleys through which small rivers rush over rocky beds and cascade over frequent waterfalls. A smaller lake formed near Scarborough, the Hackness Lake, and its overflow channel carved the picturesque Forge Valley. All these waters flowing south met to form Lake Pickering across what is now the Vale of Pickering, the wide flat valley which separates the Moors from the Wolds. As Lake Pickering itself overflowed near Kirkham, melt-water surged down the Vale of York. Undercutting at the western escarpment of the Moors caused a cliff slip at Sutton Bank. Melt-water was trapped in a depression surrounded by slipped material eroded from the cliff. Hence we have the ancient origin of Gormire Lake one of Yorkshire's only three natural lakes.

As the Moors emerged from their frozen blanket, hardy arctic species migrated from the south and reached the Moors. These plants colonised the cold wet soils at the edge of the snow. For several thousand years this arctic-alpine tundra flowered freely and dominated the landscape. With further amelioration of the climate the coniferous trees were able to advance northwards and shade out the low herbaceous alpine turf. In this Country this boreal forest was composed mainly of Scots Pine *(Pinus sylvestris)* and Birch *(Betula sp.)*. Deciduous trees soon followed in the wake of evergreen. Longer lived than Scots Pine deciduous trees gradually replaced the conifer and the high tableland, ancient valley and newly created melt-water valleys were clothed with deciduous woodland dominated by Birch and Sessile Oak *(Quercus petraea)*.

It is perhaps surprising that several of these cool-climate arctic plants have persisted over thousands of years and can still be found on the Moors. These species have survived from the Late Glacial Flora. Often the persistence of relict arctic-alpine vegetation below the 2,000 ft tree line can be explained by a total absence of trees on such sites. In the case of the famous relict populations of Teesdale unstable soils over sugar limestone were unsuitable for trees, and alpine flowers have grown there in full sunshine for 10,000 years. In the West Riding high steep limestone scars were a similar treeless refuge for members of the arctic-alpine flora. The presence of northern plants such as Dwarf Cornel *(Cornus suecica)*, (Plate 1) Small White Orchid *(Leucorchis albida)*, Mountain Everlasting *(Antennaria dioica)* and Chickweed Wintergreen *(Trientalis europaeus)* has never been adequately explained. The only unique feature of the habitats in which these plants grow appears to be the occurrence of the plants themselves. Perhaps these flowers are not as intolerant of forest shade as are many members of the mountain flora. Certainly the Small White Orchid and the Chickweed Wintergreen will thrive in natural Pine woodlands. The occurrence of such rarities in the Park invites thought and speculation.

At this point man enters the stage. Searching for village sites, he rejected the lowlands which were still swamp and lakeland from melt-water accumulation. These wet lowlands must have been the breeding ground of insects and disease. Instead he sought the high dry uplands and created his settlements on the Moors. To give warning of the approach of adversaries he would burn or fell the trees around his village to give a clear distant view of any aggressor.

PLATE 1
Dwarf Cornel *(Cornus suecica)*, a rare survivor from the late glacial flora.

Fire was a useful tool to drive out game animals. Man became a primitive farmer. He sowed his crops in small, cleared areas near his village and when natural fertility was exhausted and crops failed he would move on to an adjacent site and clear more woodland. The concept of returning nutrients to a depleted soil with manure or other fertiliser was an unknown technology to this primitive man. With this so-called shifting agriculture cleared areas gradually spread across the landscape. Over hundreds, leading to thousands of years populations increased, farming efficiency increased and by the Bronze Age much of the woodland on the Moors had disappeared. Today all that remains of this ancient woodland are remnants on steep-sided valleys, by streamside and crag where agriculture was not a practicable proposition.

Heather *(Calluna vulgaris)* was a common understorey plant in the ancient forest and in our oceanic climate, and free of forest shade the plant thrived and multiplied. Heather is ideally suited to growth in mild damp climates near the sea. Man set the seal to the success of Heather. Firstly the Moorland sheep was allowed to graze the Moor and then grouse shooting became the sport of Kings on the killing field of the moors. Young succulent Heather shoots are the staple diet of both the sheep and grouse. Burning keeps the Heather young and also destroys any woody invader and this practice has fashioned our present Moorland landscape. Dark and sombre for much of the year the Moors dress themselves in bright purple and hum with bees with the flowering of the Heather in August.

Since 1921 large areas of the Moorland have been ploughed and planted with conifers. The Forestry Commission controls over 50,000 acres of the Moorland and over 90% of this land is planted with trees. Most of these plantations are in the south-east corner of the National Park. Scots Pine was the first tree to be planted, but since the 1950's Lodgepole Pine *(Pinus contorta)* and Sitka Spruce *(Picea sitchensis)* have been favoured. Both these trees are native to the western coast of North America where they thrive in a similar oceanic climate. The Dalby Forest with its picnic sites and nature trails is a popular haunt of holiday makers from Scarborough.

On the southern edge of the Moors the landscape and geology change dramatically as we drop from the moors and see the north facing escarpment of the Tabular Hills. Attractive valleys and flat-

PLATE 2
The Cleveland Hills over ripening wheat.

12

topped hills stretch from Scarborough to Helmsley and then blend into the Hambleton Hills which skirt the south-west edge of the Park and rise above the Vale of York. Now we are entering limestone country, always a marvellous terrain for finding flowers, and none more so than the Corallian Limestone bands of the North Yorkshire Moors National Park. From Forge Valley to Sutton Bank we can find calcareous habitats from primary woodland and streamside marsh to dry grassland yellow with Cowslips *(Primula veris)*. Rich in the number of different flower species these areas have many affinities with the Carboniferous Limestone of the Pennines.

Travelling north from the Hambleton Hills we approach the impressive range of the Cleveland Hills (Plate 2) forming the edge of the Park in the north west and on, eastwards towards the coast. The Cleveland Hills have a long history of quarrying for ironstone and alum. Roseberry Topping is perhaps the most noticeable feature of this line of hills, but the distinctive shape of this hill is the result of landslips above the 19th century ironstone mines. At Black Hambleton, above Osmotherley, we leave any outcrops of limestone and return to the acid soils and plants that are familiar across the plateau and valleys of the Moors themselves.

The coastline of the Park is very spectacular, of high cliff and sheltered bay. The exposed cliff strata of the Yorkshire Coast has been a Mecca for geologists for over 200 years and, as always, a complex and varied geology has resulted in an equally complex sequence of habitats. With soils varying from acidic to calcareous the cliff vegetation of the Park can offer a tremendous variety of flowers.

In essence, few areas of similar size in Britain can boast such a varied array of wild flowers, from seaside Orache, to mountain Orchid, from boggy Cotton Grass to calcareous Rockrose. The North Yorkshire Moors National Park is of exceptional interest to anyone interested in wild flowers. The plants mentioned in the following chapters are taken from my recent records collected since 1975, and the habitats are described from a much longer familiarity with a countryside that has fascinated me from childhood.

THE MOORS

The Moors themselves cover the greatest land area in the Park and it is appropriate to consider their flora first. The Moors are a flat sandstone tableland dissected by many small valleys. These valleys were formed about 10–11,000 years ago by water erosion at the end of the Ice Age, when the waters from the melting snow fought their way down to the lowlands. These same valleys are now the channels for fast-flowing streams which drop from the high plateau by a series of waterfalls.

The spring lies cold on this windswept Moor and the flora awaits the heightening summer sun. Thus for much of the year these uplands present a dark monotonous landscape but, in the late summer heat with the shortening days of July a purple tide washes over the hillside. Alight with colour and singing with bees the heather blossoms transform the face of the Moors. The natural vegetation of the sandstone moor is Sessile Oak *(Quercus petraea)* and Birch *(Betula sp.)* woodland. Man felled or burned this woodland many centuries ago and the plateau became dominated by members of the heath family (Ericaceae).

In recent centuries the Moors have been managed for sheep rearing and as grouse moors and are covered acre following acre by one species of flowering plant, Heather *(Calluna vulgaris)*. This plant is the supreme opportunist and aggressor in the moorland environment (Plates 3 and 4). Following the work by Dimbleby on pollen analysis on the Moors, it is generally accepted that the clearance of the forest occurred around the Bronze Age. Heather was one of the prominent understorey shrubs in the native Sessile Oak woodland. Climatic tolerance of Heather labels it as an oceanic plant, only able to survive in an open treeless environment in Britain, and the western seaboards of Northern Europe. In the Continental climatic extremes it will always demand tree protection for successful growth. In the treeless landscape that followed clearance, rainfall was no longer intercepted by canopy foliage and

14

PLATE 3
Bell Heather *(Erica cinerea)* the flower of the driest sandstone ridges.

15

PLATE 4
Cross Leaved Heather *(Erica tetralix)* the flower of wet heathland.

pounded unhindered on the herbaceous ground cover over the light sandy soils. Iron and nutrients were washed through the surface layers, and soils became infertile. Having lost the equilibrating influence of tree cover the soils suffered extremes of drought in periods of low rainfall, followed by waterlogging and flooding after seasonal storms. Heather alone achieved the dominating influence over this changing deteriorating environment. Slow growing, it requires few nutrients and has a fungal root infection which increases its nitrogen and phosphorus supply. As an evergreen it has small waxy leaves which resist desiccation; they also decay slowly and contain organic acids which accelerate nutrient loss from the sandy soils. Each Heather plant is also capable of ripening thousands of seeds which can germinate with a high success rate.

Large populations of Grouse depend upon a good supply of young Heather shoots and consequently the Moors are burned frequently in controlled management schemes. Under this regime the litter does not accumulate to any great extent. Dead litter is the powder keg for any moorland fire and in its absence the fire sweeps rapidly but briefly over any one locale and heat intensity is relatively low. Contrast this with the drought summer of 1976 when fires raged long and powerfully over parts of our Moors as well as over heathlands elsewhere in the country. The heat generated over the parched landscape ignited the peat itself which smouldered for several weeks. No vegetation can survive *in situ* under such conditions. After the usual controlled burning Heather regenerates quickly from ground level buds which are protected in the shallow litter. This response of Heather to burning has been manipulated by man in his management of the Moors for Grouse rearing. The Grouse thrives on young regenerating Heather shoots which are rich in essential minerals, and nests in older taller heather plants. The territory of a nesting pair must contain both young and old Heather. Thus the Grouse moor manager burns the moors in strips to provide heather of various ages; the patchwork quilt of blacks, browns and greens is a familiar sight on the moorland tops. If by accident the intensity of the fire is hot enough to damage the Heather buds at the ground surface, and effectively kill the parent, then the blackened acid moorland is a perfect seed bed for germinating Heather seeds. Thus Heather has a unique recipe for success in the moorland habitat, capitalising on man-induced

17

environmental change.

The main competitor for ascendancy in moorland vegetation patterns is Bracken *(Pteridium aquilinum)*. Many people believe that Bracken is spreading on the moors. This successful fern is sensitive to high winds which break and desiccate its fronds, and seems to prefer deep soils. Bracken in the hollows and Heather on the tops would be an easily explained zonal pattern. Unfortunately, on the ground the pattern is not so rigid and the actual competitive balance between the two must be more complex. In medieval times cows were grazed as commonly as sheep and Bracken was collected by farmers and used as bedding for livestock in the winter. The fronds of Bracken are actually poisonous to stock. However moorland sheep cannot graze on the long fronds and favour the Heather shoots. Thus it is possible that changing land use may partially explain the spread of Bracken with the disappearance of the cows. It is true that like its rival Heather, Bracken has an impressive arsenal for successful growth. The deep underground rhizome allows rapid vegetative spread and regeneration after fire. It has been shown that washings from the frond are poisonous to seedling growth of other plants. Thus the frond forms an umbrella, and the area under its shade is free from germinating competitors. Bracken does die back each autumn and must store large amounts of food in the underground rhizome to supply the energy for rapid growth in the spring. This life-style makes the plant very susceptible to cutting during the summer, just as rapid spring growth ceases, at a time when food supplies in the rhizome reach their lowest ebb. This would normally be the time of year when food produced in the frond is channelled back into the root system to be used in the following spring. Cutting the Bracken will prevent this replenishment and weaken the plant. Repetition of this cutting over several seasons will probably result in the retreat of Bracken and the advance of members of the Heath family.

Bilberry *(Vaccinium myrtillus)* can only dominate the moorland vegetation on the driest most acidic sandstone ridges. Across the moorland as a whole the Bilberry has a successful life-style which allows it to flourish among the Heather shoots and Bracken fronds. More deeply rooted than Heather it taps moisture and nutrients which are unavailable to the Heather. Bilberry leaves can grow and produce food efficiently under the shade of the Heather or Bracken (Figure 1).

18

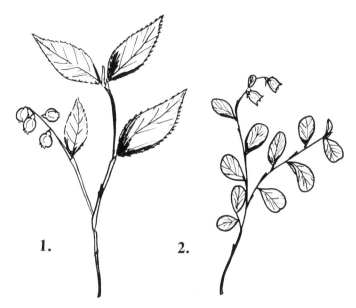

1. **2.**

FIGURE 1   Contrasting foliage of 1. Bilberry *(Vaccinium myrtillus)* and 2. Cowberry *(Vaccinium vitisidaea)* which are often found growing together on the moors.

The moorland habitat is unique in being dominated by members of only one family of flowering plant, the Ericaceae. Heather dominates in moderate soil conditions, neither too wet nor too dry. On the driest ridges Bell Heather *(Erica cinerea)* (Plate 3) joins Bilberry. In waterlogged soils poisons accumulate and lack of oxygen can cause root death. Heather cannot tolerate these conditions and it may be replaced by Cross Leaved Heather *(Erica tetralix)*. This plant of wet sites is able to exude a protective oxygen sheath which insulates the living roots from the deadly conditions in the soil. The anticipated zoning between Bell Heather and Cross Leaved Heather is often difficult to interpret in the field when they can sometimes be found growing side by side. Here identification can be difficult. Although Cross Leaved Heather has leaves in whorls of four, and Bell Heather in whorls of three, growth of axillary buds often makes leaf arrangement difficult to see. These two plants are more easily differentiated by the paler pink of the Cross Leaved Heather flowers and its very hairy leaves and sepals. In contrast, the leaves and sepals of Bell Heather are hairless.

19

Constant members of the moorland community

Heather	*Calluna vulgaris*
Bracken	*Pteridium aquilinum*
Bilberry	*Vaccinium myrtillus*
Bell Heather	*Erica cinerea*
Cross Leaved Heather	*Erica tetralix*
Cowberry	*Vaccinium vitis-idaea*
Crowberry	*Empetrum nigrum*
Tormentil	*Potentilla erecta*
Heath Bedstraw	*Galium saxatile*
Harebell	*Campanula rotundifolia*
Sheep's Sorrel	*Rumex acetosa*

The common names given to many members of the heathland cause problems for the beginner who would be well advised to commit the latin names to memory. Bilberry, Cowberry, Crowberry, trip off the tongue of the seasoned naturalist in quick succession. The evergreen Cowberry *(Vaccinium vitis-idaea)* can be easily distinguished from deciduous Bilberry *(Vaccinium myrtillus)* on foliage characters alone (Figure 1). Cowberry is quite common; the delicate pink May flowers form bright red fruits later in the summer which are not as palatable as the black Bilberry. The black berries of Crowberry *(Empetrum nigrum)* are favoured by birds rather than man; the foliage is distinguished by tightly rolled leaves which arise singly along the stem. On the underside of the leaves the gap between the rolled margins gives the appearance of a white strip and this is the easiest identification feature.

The nitrogen supply in these moorland soils is low; the plants which have a successful life on the heath have an additional source of nitrogen. Heather has a fungal infection inside its root cells which creates an extra supply of nitrogen. The hyphal threads of the fungus possibly create a larger absorption surface for taking in soil nitrogen; also acids secreted by the fungus into the soil have the ability to dissolve soil nitrogen. These acids are special to the fungus and cannot be produced by the root cells themselves. In return for help with nitrogen supply the Heather feeds the fungus with some of the sugars that it manufactures in its sunlit leaves using the photosynthetic process. This co-operative relationship between a fungus and a plant root is called a mycorrhizae, and is very common among plants frequenting poor soils. In many such relationships the fungus forms a weft over the plant root rather than inside the cells as is the case in Heather. The Legume family, e.g. peas, vetches etc., have a bacterial infection in their roots, housed in root nodules. These are nitrogen fixing bacteria which supply the plant with this scarce commodity. Not surprisingly this family is well represented on the Moorland, from carpets of Bird's Foot Trefoil *(Lotus corniculatus)* on grassy sheep tracks, to prickly Gorse *(Ulex europaeus)* on exposed hillsides, and Broom *(Cytisus scoparius)* on sandy embankments. All these yellow flowered members of the Leguminosae are common on the moor. Petty Whin *(Genista anglica)* is of more local occurrence but can be found on the edge of the moorland in central and eastern areas of the Park (Nan Sykes record).

The tall red spikes of Foxglove *(Digitalis purpurea)* are a common sight on the moors, and down among the Heather shoots you can always find Tormentil *(Potentilla erecta)* and a white carpet of Heath Bedstraw *(Galium saxatile)*. Tormentil is unique among the yellow cinquefoils in usually having only four petals instead of five. The plant can vary tremendously in stature; a few centimetres tall in grazed grassland it can exceed 25cm when it grows up through heathland scrub in search of light. These colourful herbs of the heathland will be more common in areas where the Heather is old with more woody twigs and hence where there is more opportunity for light to reach the small plants growing under the Heather canopy. Few plants can compete with vigorously growing Heather three, four or five years after a controlled burn.

Frequent members of this community

Climbing Corydalis	*Corydalis claviculata*
Beautiful St. John's Wort	*Hypericum pulchrum*
Devil's Bit Scabious	*Succisa pratensis*
Wood Sorrel	*Oxalis acetosella*
Heath Spotted Orchid	*Dactylorhiza maculata*

Occasional/Rare members of this community

Chickweed Wintergreen	*Trientalis europaeus*
Cow Wheat	*Melampyrum pratense*
Dwarf Cornel	*Cornus suecica*

21

Chickweed Wintergreen *(Trientalis europaeus)* is a familiar plant of Scottish pine woodland but in certain areas of the Moor has a short flowering season in June among the new growth of Heather or Bracken. Dwarf Cornel *(Cornus suecica)* is a famous rarity of the Moors, and is more familiar to the rambler in the Scottish mountains. Indeed this attractive flower (Plate 1) has its southernmost location in Britain on these moors.

In spite of the occurrence of occasional and puzzling rarities the moorland community of flowers is not very diverse. Rambles across the windswept tops of the Moor often reveal a monotonous regularity of less than a dozen flowering plants. The views across the moor are frequently more varied than the plants and on a clear windy day distant vistas across this high wide tableland carry the eye from coastal moors in the east to the Hambleton Hills above the Vale of York.

FACTS AND FICTION

Heather *(Calluna vulgaris)*
Calluna is derived from the Greek word meaning broom, the tough woody stems being traditionally tied together to make a besom. Heather was also used for thatching. Honey from Heather flowers is a local cottage industry and such honey is reputed to be a tranquiliser.

Cowberry *(Vaccinium vitis-idaea)*
The red berries are said to stimulate appetite. The plant yields a yellow dye and a tea made from the leaves is said to be effective against rheumatism.

Tormentil *(Potentilla erecta)*
This little flower is one of the many cinquefoils. This group was used by witches as an ingredient of 'Flying ointment', which was rubbed over their bodies to give them the power of flight. Tormentil roots contain tannin and have been chewed to harden the gums and keep the mouth clear of infection. The plant has blood coagulating properties and has also been used to cure colic, diarrhoea and cystitis.

22

Foxglove *(Digitalis purpurea)*
The medicinal uses of the plant in heart conditions was first discovered by William Withering a Birmingham physician of the late 18th century. The powdered leaves are the source of digitalis which is administered as a cardiac tonic, sedative and heart stimulant. The plant is of course very poisonous and can cause death. A favourite explanation for the common name of this plant is that bad fairies gave the flowers to foxes to put on their paws so that they could creep silently up to their prey.

BOG

Let us turn our attention to the wet depressions on the Moors where centuries of waterlogging have led to peat formation and a surface with bog vegetation. Formation and maintenance of bog vegetation is dependent upon the health and vitality of the Bog Moss *(Sphagnum* sp.*)*. Given adequate rainfall, probably in excess of 150cm this moss can grow and spread across the landscape using only rainwater for both moisture and nutrient supply. A bog which receives all its water from rain is called ombrotrophic. Sphagnum acts as a sponge and in wet weather the leaves contain many times their own weight of water. The rainfall of the North Yorkshire Moors is not usually adequate for ombrotrophic bog formation, and to succeed the Bog Moss requires additional sources of low-base status run-off from the surrounding landscape. In simple terms, on the moors, bog vegetation can occur in hollows or valleys where rainfall is supplemented by run off from the surrounding sandstone and drainage is impeded. Over the centuries water-logging has prevented plant decay and has resulted in peat formation. Although peats to a depth of 20 metres can be found in some areas of the Moor it is more common for the peat to form a thin layer over the sandstone.

In such waterlogged, nutrient poor conditions Bog Moss can thrive and with it we find the typical flowers associated with a bog.

Cross Leaved Heather	*Erica tetralix*
Bog Asphodel	*Narthecium ossifragum*
Round Leaved Sundew	*Drosera rotundifolia*
Butterwort	*Pinguicula vulgaris*
Bog Myrtle	*Myrica gale*
Lousewort	*Pedicularis sylvatica*
Purple Moor Grass	*Molinia caerulea*
Heath Spotted Orchid	*Dactylorhiza maculata*

The small shrubs of Bog Myrtle *(Myrica gale)* bear catkins on red stems which are conspicuous before the leaves open. Superficially the shrub could be confused with a willow, but the leaves are delightfully aromatic, a feature not shared with any of the willows. You may find the Bog Myrtle growing with Eared Willow *(Salix aurita)*. This shrub willow is tolerant of acid wet soils and is named from the conspicuous paired stipules which look like ears at the base of each leaf stalk.

With the flowering of the Bog Asphodel *(Narthecium ossifragum)* (Plate 5) the surface of the bog is splashed with the vivid yellow of thousands of blooms. This plant comes into flower in late June to early July and the fruiting heads are a noticeable feature of the bog well into the autumn. Among the Asphodels one can frequently find the pink and white heads of Heath Spotted Orchid *(Dactylorhiza maculata)*. Very few orchids can compete with other vegetation in the harsh environment of an acid upland, but Heath Spotted Orchid thrives here and is absent from the lush lowland meadow.

The vast majority of flowering green plants convert carbon dioxide into sugar by using energy from the sun harnessed by the green pigment of the leaf *(chlorophyll)*. The other nutrients and minerals needed for healthy growth are taken up by the roots with the water of the soil solution. Some of these nutrients are required in large amounts e.g. nitrogen, phosphorus, potassium, and others in minute quantities e.g. iron, magnesium and aluminium. The keen gardener increases the nutrient supply available in his garden soil by the addition of fertilisers which are usually a base of nitrogen, phosphorus and potassium. Bog Moss akin with other mosses, lacks well differentiated roots and can absorb nutrients available in rain or ground water over the whole of its vast leaf area. Bog Moss species are unique in that this completed absorption process results in the increased acidity of the surrounding bog pool water. This creates an inhospitable environment for the growth of most plant competitors. There are many different species of Bog Moss, but identification is difficult and usually requires examination with a microscope. Two unrelated groups of British land plants are also partially independent of ground water supply of nutrients. Butterwort *(Pinguicula vulgaris)* and Round Leaved Sundew *(Drosera rotundifolia)* are able to feed off the bodies of insects to supplement the meagre supply of nutrients available in the bog. Round Leaved Sundew is common on the surface of bogs in the

PLATE 5
Bog Asphodel *(Narthecium ossifragum)* can carpet a bog with yellow flowers
in July.

26

Park. The leaves lie flat to the surface and are covered in glandular hairs. Each hair secretes a droplet of glistening liquid which attracts insects on the look-out for water in which to lay their eggs. This fluid is sticky and holds the insect while the hairs curl over to trap the insect in a barred condemned cell. The plant then secretes juices which convert the soft parts of the insect's body into nutrient rich soup which the leaf can then absorb. The appetite of the Sundew is voracious, catching several hundred insects every summer month. The tiny delicate white flowers of the Sundew are borne in clusters on a thin stem. Opening in July these flowers have a gentle, ethereal beauty presenting a vivid contrast to the activities of the leaves beneath. The Common Butterwort relies on a sticky fluid to hold its victims fast. This glue is secreted from glandular hairs on the surface of light green rosetted leaves. Digestion of nutrients in the insect follows in the same pattern as with the Sundew. The Butterwort has attractive showy purple-blue flowers which open in June. Sundews are found in the poorest of sites where growth of luxuriant vegetation is limited by nutrient deficiency. Butterwort is more ubiquitous and can compete with the more vigorous fen vegetation, discovered in wet sites boasting a higher supply of nutrients in the bog water. Thus Butterwort can be found in acid bogs around Goathland but also in the herbaceous fens of the limestone belt circling the southern edge of the Moors.

In waterlogged soils air spaces between the soil particles are filled with water. Living healthy roots require air for respiration and anaerobic conditions in the bog prevent most rooted plants from surviving. In waterlogged soils the roots of Heather die. As discussed in the Moorland chapter, Cross Leaved Heather *(Erica tetralix)* exudes oxygen from its roots and is the heather best suited for growth in the bog. Cotton Grass *(Eriophorum angustifolium)* whose white cottony heads are such a feature of the bog, also has the ability to protect its roots with exuded oxygen. This enables Cotton Grass to grow in the wettest of sites very successfully. The closely related Hare's Tail Sedge *(Eriophorum vaginatum)* is common on slightly drier sites than its relative and can be distinguished from Cotton Grass by having only one cottony, fruiting head instead of the several heads present in Cotton Grass.

Of the berry-bearing shrubs encompassed within the Vaccinium genus, Cranberry *(Vaccinium oxycoccus)* is ideally suited to trailing growth across the surface of the bog. With artificial drainage of wetlands the Cranberry is becoming a rare species and the berries should on no account be collected for sauce making. Supermarket cranberry sauce is cheap, tasty and made from the large berries of commercially grown North American Cranberry. Bog Rosemary *(Andromeda polifolia)* is one of the rarest bog plants in Britain. This pink bell member of the heath family is one of the first plants eliminated when man disturbs the bog surface by burning, draining or overgrazing. Now restricted to probably one area it is not a bog plant that the rambler is likely to come upon by chance. Deterioration of the bog due to burning may seem a strange concept when one imagines the water charged surface in the rainy season. However in a dry summer the surface layers of Bog Moss dry out and are very quick to burn. Burn scars may cut deep into the moss carpet and create runoff and drainage channels which can be made deeper and more disastrous by future rain storms.

The Sedge flora of the bog is rich and varied; the commonest members of this family are well within the capabilities of the beginner in plant identification. Star Sedge *(Carex echinata)* is particularly common on the Moors and should be looked for in any acid wet sites.

Star Sedge	*Carex echinata*
Common Sedge	*Carex nigra*
Flea Sedge	*Carex pulicaris*
Lesser Pond Sedge	*Carex acutiformis*
Green Ribbed Sedge	*Carex binervis*
White Beak Sedge	*Rhynchospora alba*
Cotton Grass	*Eriophorum angustifolium*
Hare's Tail Sedge	*Eriophorum vaginatum*

FACTS AND FICTION

Bog Asphodel *(Narthecium ossifragum)*
Dye obtained from the brilliant yellow flowers has been used to dye the hair. It is ideally adapted to dispersal in wet habitats, since the seeds which mature with the rains of autumn have floats which give buoyancy allowing them to float to new habitats in flood water.

Lousewort *(Pedicularis sylvatica)*
This horrible name was given to this rather attractive plant because farmers believed that sheep which ate lousewort were verminous. More likely that sheep feeding on such poor pasturage were weakened and susceptible to infestation. I have read in a French identification book that the real reason for the name is that the foliage of louseworts will keep lice away! I have never been prepared to test the truth of the last statement.

Bog Myrtle *(Myrica gale)*
This shrub has a powerful balsamic perfume and was used in the Middle Ages to flavour beer. It has also been used to polish furniture and to make aromatic candles. Countryfolk have long used the leaves to repel insects, a property worth remembering when you visit a high summer bog alive with biting insects.

ACID WOODLAND

When man first explored the North Yorkshire Moors after the last Ice Age his distant views from the high sandstone bluffs would have unfolded a very different landscape from that of the 20th century. The dissected sandstone plateau that underlies the Moors was covered and camouflaged by deciduous woodland dominated by Sessile Oak *(Quercus petraea)* and Birch *(Betula sp.)*. Today after millenia of forest clearance the woodlands of the moors are largely restricted to the slopes of the steep-sided valleys which cut deep into the plateau. These woodlands are still dominated by Sessile Oak and Birch, with Alder *(Alnus glutinosa)* and Sallow *(Salix cinerea)* becoming more important near the streams where the soil is more moist. Numerous additional tree species occur with these dominants and include both British trees:—

Hazel	*Corylus avellana*
Mountain Ash	*Sorbus aucuparia*
Hawthorn	*Crataegus monogyna*
Beech	*Fagus sylvatica*

and introduced species:—

Larch	*Larix europaea*
Sycamore	*Acer pseudoplatanus*

The understorey flowers of the mixed oak woodland are not generally as exciting as those of the limestone woodlands on the southern edge of the Moors. However it would be wrong to dismiss these relict woodlands, since they offer a wealth of herbaceous flowers. Woodland flowers to be found around Goathland include:—

Dog's Mercury	*Mercurialis perennis*
Woodruff	*Galium odorata*

30

PLATE 6
Heather *(Calluna vulgaris)* in flower across Bransdale.

31

PLATE 7
Common Spotted Orchid *Dactylorhiza fuchsii)* in a wet pasture.

32

Wood Sorrel	*Oxalis acetosella*
Wood Anemone	*Anemone nemorosa*
Yellow Pimpernel	*Lysimachia nemorum*
Wood Sanicle	*Sanicula europaea*
Bugle	*Ajuga reptans*
Cow Wheat	*Melampyrum pratense*
Bluebell	*Hyacinthoides non-scripta*
Foxglove	*Digitalis purpurea*
Great Woodrush	*Luzula sylvatica*
Pignut	*Conopodium majus*
Cuckoo Pint	*Arum maculatum*
Heather	*Calluna vulgaris*
Bilberry	*Vaccinium myrtillus*

The woodland slopes grading down to the streams show an interesting mixture of flowers, among them those considered to be most typical of acid soils e.g. Bilberry and those associated with calcareous soils e.g. Cuckoo Pint *(Arum maculatum)*.

These steep woodland slopes have been relatively undisturbed by man and are often free from coppice or plantation. Many naturalists have been nurtured with a love of, and familiarity with the country-side, but how often the wilderness haunts of youth have disappeared under crop, forestry plantation or drainage scheme. It is very depressing and the active conservationist can only work usefully with an attitude of optimism. I recently made a pilgrimage to a favourite place of my youth, a steep-sided wooded ravine near Kildale. To my delight the scene was an unchanged, unspoilt mirror of the past: cliff sides clothed with ancient ferns and tangled tree roots, dropping to a gentle stony river; riverside flats deep in Flag *(Iris pseudacorus)* Great Hairy Willow Herb *(Epilobium hirsutum)* and Angelica *(Angelica sylvestris)*. It is the river Leven that flows down this valley and ultimately cascades down an attractive waterfall framed in trees. This river flows to the north and is the last and yet longest of the tributaries of the Tees. The variety of trees found in the wood is surprising, with Rhododendron *(Rhododendron ponticum)* and Crab Apple *(Malus sylvestris)* being added to those trees previously listed. The presence of Greater Bellflower *(Campanula latifolia)* (Plate 9) along the river bank probably indicates enriched soil conditions from recurrent spate of the river in times of heavy rainfall. As a child, unconcerned with species variety or rarity, the

33

PLATE 8
The hamlet of Darnholm near Goathland.

34

woodland was a dense jungle of luxuriant foliage with woody climber and exposed roots from which to cling and tumble. The valley is an oasis of natural beauty in an area containing many acres of Forestry Commission plantation.

The woodlands on such steep river banks are primary woodland. It is not surprising that a number of rarities have persisted in parts of these woodland remnants.

Whilst most orchids prefer neutral to alkaline soils, a few members of this family shun the rich woodland or grassland of the limestone to prefer the acid soils over the sandstone of the Moors themselves. Lesser Twayblade *(Listera cordata)* is such a flower and though not restricted to shady sites it thrives in deep shade by a river bank near Goathland. Clearly the site is an ancient woodland. Twayblades can be differentiated from other orchids by their possession of only one pair of broad opposite leaves. In the Lesser Twayblade this pair of leaves is held above the ground and the plant has small reddish-green flowers that look like little men, complete with head, arms and legs. Lesser Twayblade is rarer than its relative Common Twayblade *(Listera ovata)* which frequents neutral to calcareous grassland and woodland. The Common Twayblade is a larger plant with more numerous and green little men. Differences between the two species are shown in Figure 2.

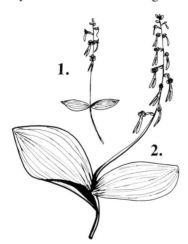

FIGURE 2   Contrasting growth form and flower shape of the two Twayblades, 1. Lesser Twayblade *(Listera cordata)* and 2. Common Twayblade *(Listera ovata)*.

The smaller Lesser Twayblade blends into the background and is easily overlooked. Plants associated with the Lesser Twayblade in this woodland site include:—

Heather	*Calluna vulgaris*
Bilberry	*Vaccinium myrtillus*
Hard Fern	*Blechnum spicant*
Male Fern	*Dryopteris filix-mas*

under a canopy of:—

Silver Birch	*Betula pendula*
Mountain Ash	*Sorbus aucuparia*
Sessile Oak	*Quercus petraea*

In general only inaccessible woodlands have been left undisturbed. The Yorkshire Wildlife Trust has a 34-acre reserve of scrub oak woodland on the steep coastal cliffs around Hayburn Wyke. The forest was once more extensive but now only the 100 metre cliffs are clothed in natural woodland. Trees surviving on such an exposed coast are of course extremely wind shorn and dwarfed in character. A more 'natural' stand of Sessile Oak can be seen along the valleys of the Bridestones Nature Reserve in the Dalby Forest.

These woodlands serve as a vivid reminder of the dramatic effect man has had on the landscape. On the purple windswept moors man's ceiling is the stormy sky of the distant horizon; how different in the cool green cloisters of the wooded glade where the elements are tempered by the trees and the traveller encircled by their protection.

One can hardly fail to notice that the most extensive areas of woodland on the moors are not of native deciduous trees but of fast growing conifers which have no place in the natural ecosystem. The forestry plantations of the Park comprise one of the largest tracts of coniferous forest on upland heath in England. Planting began in 1921 and recently the expansive phase has ceased as the early planted trees come to maturity. Thus the Forestry Commission owns vast areas of the Moors and one of their stated aims is to achieve a pattern of rural land use which encompasses farming and recreation within their boundaries. Scots Pine *(Pinus sylvestris)* was

PLATE 9
Greater Bellflower *(Campanula latifolia)* is frequent in woodland and hedgerow.

37

the favoured species until the 1950's when it was superseded by Lodgepole Pine *(Pinus contorta)* and later by Sitka Spruce *(Picea sitchensis)*. Establishment of productive forest on the barren soils of the acid heathland was not always easy. Hard iron pans beneath the surface had to be cracked by deep ploughing, drainage conditions had to be modified and establishment of fungal infections in young tree roots was often a necessary prerequisite for healthy growth in the nitrogen poor soils (see page 20).

When the plantations have been sited over poor upland heath the loss to the natural history of the Moors may not have been great. The forest provides shelter and food for mammals and birds and increases the diversity of available habitats. Forestry plantations over calcareous soils are much more disturbing and must have resulted in significant losses to our valuable calcareous flora. On such sites around the Tabular Hills or near Helmsley the previous botanical interest of the site can only be gauged by the wealth of species living a precarious existence in the illuminated woodland rides. The deep shade of the conifer plantation will only allow the growth of moss, fern and perhaps the odd plant of Wood Sorrel *(Oxalis acetosella)*. Near Thornton Dale the Forestry woodlands cross from sandstone soils into the limestone belt and Rock Rose *(Helianthemum chamaecistus)* and Salad Burnet *(Poterium sanguisorba)* can be found at the edge of the pine canopy. Occasionally, rarities have managed to persist in the forestry belts; Chickweed Wintergreen *(Trientalis europaeus)* grows in coniferous woodland near Hackness and streamside habitats have provided a refuge for Mountain Fern *(Oreopteris limbosperma)* near Harwood Dale. For the most part the grassy forest ride through coniferous plantations on acid soils offers little to interest the botanist except perhaps for the occasional Tormentil *(Potentilla erecta)*, Wood Sage *(Teucrium scorodonia)*, Devil's Bit Scabious *(Succisa pratensis)* and Sneezewort *(Achillea ptarmica)*. The wet drainage ditch by the side of the forestry road is often worth exploring.

Common plants by the track:—

Common Centaury	*Centaurium erythraea*
Conglomerate Rush	*Juncus conglomeratus*
Jointed Rush	*Juncus articulatus*
Marsh Thistle	*Cirsium palustre*

38

Brooklime	*Veronica beccabunga*
Water Blinks	*Montia fontana*
Wavy Bittercress	*Cardamine flexuosa*
Bog Stitchwort	*Stellaria alsine*
Common Spotted Orchid	*Dactylorhiza fuchsii*

Forestry Commission plantations are often unpopular with both naturalist and rambler, but it is important to remember the value of these plantations to the rural economy of the area. Forestry supports a much larger work force per unit area than sheep or grouse moor.

FACTS AND FICTION

Wood Sanicle *(Sanicula europaea)*
A very important medicinal plant which from the 12th century was a popular treatment for wounds. The plant does contain active chemicals, saponin and tannins. The plant was also dried, infused in wine and taken as a cure for diarrhoea.

Mountain Ash *(Sorbus aucuparia)*
This is a magical plant; its other common name Rowan is thought to be a distortion of rune which means a charm. Twigs were thought to keep evil away and were hung over doorways. This tree can extend far up mountains, well above normal tree-line and can often be found nestling into crevices on mountain ledges.

Wood Anemone *(Anemone nemorosa)*
This flower has many common names Wind Flower and Thunder Flower which refer to its alternative habitat of windswept upland meadows. The plant was infused as a tea for external use in washing ulcers and sores, or as an eyewash.

Dog's Mercury *(Mercurialis perennis)*
According to Greek Legend, Mercury was the first to appreciate the healing powers of this plant. The fresh plant is a laxative and diuretic. A yellow dye has also been extracted which has been used to colour wool. Akin with all other members of the spurge family this plant is very poisonous.

LIMESTONE WOODLANDS

The limestone outcrops at the southern edges of the Park support rich woodland tracts which classically should reflect a canopy of Ash *(Fraxinus excelsior)*, the dominant native tree of northern calcareous soils. In reality the mixture of trees is much more varied than this, the presence of plantations and alien species camouflaging the native deciduous woodland. Ash casts a lighter shade than any other dominant native woodland tree and this is one of the main reasons why the flowers of the Ash woodland are more varied than any other. Although the forests contain many foreign species introduced by man over recent centuries, many tracts do not show the tell-tale signs of coppice growth which is indicative of intensively managed woodland.

The practice of cutting back deciduous trees to ground level to stimulate production of new straight branches (coppicing) goes back well beyond the Bronze Age. These poles have been useful to man for building and fencing. Although in the north Hazel *(Corylus avellana)* was the most commonly coppiced crop, all our native deciduous trees will produce long useful poles when cut back to the ground. In a managed coppice the trees are usually cut every 20 to 25 years, depending on climatic and soil conditions. The sudden explosion of light to the woodland floor which results from coppicing has encouraged growth of woodland flowers that could not tolerate the continuing deep summer shade of unmanaged woodland. In woodland which has not been regularly coppiced the vernal flora is the most interesting; this completes its flowering before the tree canopy opens. In an old coppice one might expect the presence of later flowering plants which are occasionally able to spread and multiply in the conditions which follow coppicing. When a site has been continuously wooded since the trees returned after the Ice Age it is termed primary woodland, whether or not the site has been managed for coppice. Woodland which is replanted on to ground which has been cleared of trees for several years will

40

not have a rich woodland flora. Rare woodland plants will disappear when a site is cleared and because their powers of dispersal are poor they will not return to reinstated woodland. Many tracts of primary woodland are found on this southern edge of the Moors and their herbaceous flora will bear a close resemblance to the woodland flowers of Neolithic times before major forest clearance.

The springtime woodland over the Corallian Limestone is a delightful place to welcome the new season. These woodlands are best explored in May and June when the vernal flora of colourful herbs holds the stage to capture the sunlight streaming through the gaunt branches of the awakening trees.

Common understorey herbs:—

Dog's Mercury	*Mercurialis perennis*
Wood Anemone	*Anemone nemorosa*
Wood Sorrel	*Oxalis acetosella*
Woodruff	*Galium odorata*
Bugle	*Ajuga reptans*
Enchanter's Nightshade	*Circaea lutetiana*
Golden Saxifrage	*Chrysosplenium oppositifolium*
Wild Garlic	*Allium ursinum*
Wood Avens	*Geum urbanum*
Bluebell	*Hyacinthoides non-scripta*
Red Campion	*Silene dioica*
Sweet Violet	*Viola odorata*
Wood Violet	*Viola reichenbachiana*
Lily of the Valley	*Convallaria majalis*
Wood Speedwell	*Veronica montana*
Primrose	*Primula vulgaris*
Yellow Pimpernel	*Lysimachia nemorum*
Wood Forget-me-not	*Myosotis sylvatica*
Three Nerved Sandwort	*Moerhinckia trinervia*
Ground Ivy	*Glechoma hederacea*

Carpets of Wood Anemone *(Anemone nemorosa),* Bluebells *(Hyacinthoides non-scripta)* and Wild Garlic *(Allium ursinum)* (Plate 10) follow one another through the season. Other parts of the woodland may be dominated by the delicate Wood Sorrel *(Oxalis acetosella)* or a similar white carpet may be formed by the tiny

PLATE 10 .
Wild Garlic *(Allium ursinum)* can dominate the woodland floor in spring.

clustered flowers of Woodruff *(Galium odorata)*. In woodlands above Pickering damper shady hollows are dominated by Opposite Leaved Golden Saxifrage *(Chrysosplenium oppositifolium)* which is one of the earliest flowering springtime herbs. By the sides of streams you may find the rarer Alternate Leaved Golden Saxifrage *(Chrysosplenium alternifolium)*. As their names suggest the two can be easily distinguished by their leaf arrangement. The golden saxifrages are quite unlike the rest of their family *(Saxifragaceae)* with small petal-less (5mm) flowers which have only four sepals and eight stamens.

Many of these woodlands are over steep-sided valleys dropping to streamside shallows. In Forge Valley the sides are so steep that natural terracing results from soil creep down these slopes. Wild Columbines *(Aquilegia vulgaris)* (Plate 11) bloom on these shady terraces in June, and although similar in stature to the multi-coloured garden varieties, the Wild Columbines have solid shades of purple to white. The flowers are pollinated by bumble bees which visit the flowers for the nectar at the base of the spurs. Short-tongued insects which cannot reach the nectar often cheat and bite through the spur and steal the syrup without pollinating the flower.

One of the earliest flowers to look for is the Green Hellebore *(Helleborus viride)* which flowers in early May. This is considered to be a native member of this calcareous woodland flora, although now it is quite a popular garden plant beloved of flower arrangers. A close relative Stinking Hellebore *(Helleborus foetidus)* flowers even earlier in February or March but is more often associated with plantation or farm rather than hidden in the heart of a woodland. The Stinking Hellebore is thought to be a native of the Downs south of London, but introduced to these northern climes. We can also find another very poisonous member of the buttercup family, the Baneberry *(Actaea spicata)*. This is a northern herb with flowers which are reminiscent of Wild Clematis *(Clematis vitalba)* or Meadow Rue *(Thalictrum flavum)*. Lacking petals the flower head forms a dense mass of frothy stamens, which later in the Baneberry are replaced by a branch of shiny black berries. The presence of a berry as the fruit is very unusual in the buttercup family *(Ranunculaceae)*. Indeed the typical yellow buttercup is a

PLATE 11
Wild Columbine *(Aquilegia vulgaris)* flowers in June in some limestone woodlands.

43

flower of open meadow rather than woodland shade. There is a woodland buttercup usually called Goldilocks *(Ranunculus auricomus)*. This plant is easily distinguished from open habitat buttercups since the surface of the leaf is quite hairless in contrast with the very hairy leaves of common meadow buttercups.

Carpets of wild Lily of the Valley *(Convallaria majalis)* occur in many of these limestone woodlands and will always serve as an indicator of a rich primary woodland. Each plant has only two long, pointed leaves which are conspicuous before the delicate flowering branch is visible. Be careful not to confuse the leaves with those of Wild Garlic; a quick smell of the leaf sap will make it very obvious which you have found.

Herb Paris *(Paris quadrifolia)* is an elusive member of this woodland flora. Often growing with Dog's Mercury *(Mercurialis perennis)* the green foliage and petal-less flowers can be difficult to pick out in the green light of the woodland. The leaves of Herb Paris form a ring of four which is held above a naked stem.

As the May sunlight warms the woodland floor we can find four species of violet growing under the trees. Sweet Violet *(Viola odorata)* will be in fruit, but Wood, Hairy, and Common Violets *(Viola reichenbachiana, hirta* and *riviniana)* can be found flowering within a few metres of each other. Such a wealth of violets will always indicate a primary woodland. It is in these long established forests that you can discover rare and beautiful orchids. Early purple *(Orchis mascula)* is visible for all to see who ply the woodland paths and bridleways. Both Lesser and, more rarely, Greater Butterfly Orchids *(Platanthera bifolia* and *chlorantha)* occur in the limestone woodland. The easiest way of differentiating these two flowers lies in the alignment of the pair of pollinia in the flower centre. In Lesser Butterfly these pollinia lie parallel to each other and in Greater Butterfly (Plate 12) they lie along a converging trajectory. Although Greater Butterfly usually has a larger spike with individually larger flowers, site conditions have dramatic effects on specimen size and cause difficulty in using size class for identification. Both these plants are truly perennial orchids, but they cannot readily invade new territory. Regeneration from seed takes between five and eight years for a Butterfly Orchid, and life springs from seed so tiny that it flies with the pollen across restless woodland clearings. The flower itself is pollinated by long-tongued night flying moths which are attracted by the powerful scent emitted

44

PLATE 12
Greater Butterfly *(Platanthera chlorantha)* is an elusive June flower of the
limestone woodland.

45

from the flowers at night, as well as by their luminous colour. The Fly Orchid *(Ophrys insectifera)* will be more difficult to find, not because of reduced numbers so much, as its brilliant camouflage. This orchid mimicks a female fly. The male fly will realise his mistake when he lands on the flower but the yellow mass of pollinia is already transferred to the insect's body. Pollination relies on this fly repeating his mistake and since this orchid apparently requires cross pollination to set seed, its rarity is not difficult to explain! One of the rarest orchids of the woodland is independent of daylight and can live in the deepest forest shade. Usually found under old Beech trees *(Fagus sylvatica)* the Bird's Nest Orchid *(Neottia nidus-avis)* is saprophytic on the humus of the woodland floor. The requirement for a rich damp supply of rotting vegetation will restrict its occurrence to the densest parts of the limestone wood. Bird's Nest Orchid is much commoner in Beech woods of the south of England. Rarity, brown-honey colour and deep shade make this an orchid which is difficult to find. I also believe that once pollinated the flowers disappear quickly to merge with the litter on the forest floor. A stronger biological dependence is shown by the creamy pink Toothwort *(Lathraea squamaria)* which is parasitic on tree roots in the woodland. This plant is a member of the Broomrape family and is also independent of light levels. The Toothwort usually infests Hazel or Elm *(Ulmus sp)* and has a strange sinister flower which has been likened to a dead man's hand; hence the local name of Corpse Flower.

You will be unlikely to see all these beautiful and rare flowers in any one visit to these limestone woodlands. However, a springtime visit will always be well rewarded; whether you climb woodland slopes which look east to Scarborough Bay or west to the Vale of Mowbray you will surely find a rich and varied habitat.

FACTS AND FICTION

Green Hellebore *(Helleborus viride)*
This is a poisonous plant which was used through the Middle Ages as a worm cure, although the patient was probably more at risk than the worm! Also called Felling Grass it was used by old cow doctors. The dewlap of the sick cow was pierced and bacon rind entwined with a sprig of Green Hellebore was inserted. The open

wound would drip for three weeks, and if the cow survived it became well. The poison has also been used by witches to induce hallucinations and hysteria.

Columbine *(Aquilegia vulgaris)*
This is another poisonous member of the buttercup family. Infusions of the plant have been used to treat a sore mouth or throat or to make a lotion to help rheumatism. The dried crushed leaves are reputed to kill lice.

Baneberry *(Actaea spicata)*
Also called Herb Christopher. This plant has poisonous black berries and was named after the Greek legend of Actaeon the hunter. He surprised the goddess Artemis as she was bathing and she was so angry that she changed him into a deer. Meanwhile, his deer hounds had eaten the berries of Baneberry and became maddened with their poison; seeing Actaeon in deer form they tore him to pieces. The plant was also used against bubonic plague.

Lily of the Valley *(Convallaria majalis)*
The scent of these tiny white bells is said to restore the memory and a drug has been extracted from the plant which is allied to digitalis. This drug was thought to help restore speech after cardiac arrest. Beware any temptation to break the law and dig up these wild specimens for your garden; folklore tells us you would be dead within the year.

DRY LIMESTONE GRASSLAND

The flora of the dry grassland shows many affinities with both the cool, high Pennines to the west as well as with the warmer, rolling Wolds to the south. In some respects the Corallian limestone will form a climatic intermediary between the two, with warmer temperatures and less rainfall than the Pennines and cooler temperatures than the chalk Wolds. The response of the calcareous flora to changing rock type can be very exact. This is particularly noticeable above Thornton Dale where a band of limestone is sandwiched between two layers of sandstone. The sandstone forms the floor of the valley and the summit ridges. Here within the distance of a few metres Bilberry *(Vaccinium myrtillus)* is replaced by Rock Rose

PLATE 13
Primroses *(Primula vulgaris)* are common in woodlands in May.

48

(Helianthemum chamaecystis) and Heather *(Calluna vulgaris)* by Salad Burnet *(Poterium sanguisorba)*, as you reach the limestone soils.

In common with other dry lowland grasslands this habitat is one derived from forest clearance followed by the introduction of grazing animals. Rabbits and sheep are the main grazers, and historical records indicate that these were introduced in Norman times. In most places rabbit populations have never recovered from the myxomatosis epidemic of the 1950's and the disease may indeed be presently acting as a control measure limiting population size. Shrub invasion, as well as growth of tall rank grasses eg. Tor Grass *(Brachypodium pinnatum)*, is changing the flora of this habitat. Reduction in grazing leads to increased height and reduced diversity of grassland environments. The beautiful calcareous grassland flora is intolerant of shade and gradually disappears as shrub invasion becomes dense. When areas are actively managed for conservation eg. at the Yorkshire Wildlife Trust reserve of Ellerburn Bank, it is customary to introduce sheep during the late summer when the spring flora has flowered. Sheep grazing cannot solve the problems caused by the spread of unpalatable grasses. Before 1950 these grasses were probably held in check by intensive rabbit nibbling of young shoots. Now well established, the rank grasses spread vegetatively and are not controlled by stock introduction alone.

Typical flora of a grazed grassland

Rock Rose	*Helianthemum chamaecistus*
Salad Burnet	*Poterium sanguisorba*
Quaking Grass	*Briza media*
Dropwort	*Filipendula vulgaris*
Cowslip	*Primula veris*
Thyme	*Thymus drucei*
Bird's Foot Trefoil	*Lotus corniculatus*
Eyebright	*Euphrasia officinalis*
Mouse Ear Chickweed	*Cerastium fontanum*
Hairy Violet	*Viola hirta*
Common Violet	*Viola riviniana*
Mouse Ear Hawkweed	*Hieracium pilosella*
Pignut	*Conopodium majus*
Lady's Bedstraw	*Galium verum*

Field Mouse Ear	*Cerastium arvense*
Field Woodrush	*Luzula campestris*
Glaucous Sedge	*Carex flacca*
Fairy Flax	*Linum catharticum*
Felwort	*Gentianella amarella*
Hairy Rock Cress	*Arabis hirsuta*
Barren Strawberry	*Potentilla sterilis*
Wild Strawberry	*Fragaria vesca*

The limestone grassland is a very arid habitat and many of the regular members of this community have special adaptations to either cut down water loss or increase water uptake. Rockrose has small waxy leaves which conserve water; Salad Burnet and Thyme *(Thymus drucei)* are deeply rooted to obtain any deep-seated moisture. A profusion of hairs on the foliage traps a layer of still air on the leaf and reduces water loss. Hairy Violet *(Viola hirta)*, Hairy Rock Cress *(Arabis hirsuta)* Mouse Ear Hawkweed *(Hieracium pilosella)*, and Mouse Ear Chickweed *(Cerastium fontanum)* all show this adaptation. The grassland of the summer is a sweet smelling paradise for bee and butterfly as well as the naturalist. Several aromatic herbs from the Mint family are common in the grassland. In particular the fragrant foliage and pink flowers of Thyme, Wild Basil *(Clinopodium vulgare)* and Marjoram *(Origanum vulgare)* are particularly attractive to insects. Betony *(Betonica officinalis)* is not so aromatic, but has a bright pink spike of numerous flowers which is very conspicuous. This mid summer mint of the grassland flora has been used as both herbal tobacco and tea. The grassy bank is a happy home for the Cowslip *(Primula veris)* which is the food plant for an elusive butterfly, the Duke of Burgundy Fritillary *(Hamearis lucina)*. This butterfly is rare in the north of England but has a home range in the Park flying from mid May.

Flora of the taller grassland:—

Marjoram	*Origanum vulgare*
Wild Basil	*Clinopodium vulgare*
Meadow Saxifrage	*Saxifraga granulata*
Agrimony	*Agrimonia eupatoria*
Hairy St. John's Wort	*Hypericum hirsutum*
Common St. John's Wort	*Hypericum perforatum*

50

Lady's Mantle	*Alchemilla vulgaris* agg.
Ox Eye Daisy	*Chrysanthemum leucanthemum*
Common Vetch	*Vicia sativa*
Greater Knapweed	*Centaurea scabiosa*
Black Knapweed	*Centaurea nigra*
Woolly Thistle	*Cirsium eriophorum*
Common Spotted Orchid	*Dactylorhiza fuchsii*
Common Twayblade	*Listera ovata*
Pyramid Orchid	*Anacamptis pyramidalis*
Fragrant Orchid	*Gymnadenia conopsea*
Bee Orchid	*Ophrys apifera*

The species of this longer grassland are commonly to be found in the woodland clearing or in well-illuminated woodland rides. Although untreated limestone pasture is rare one can still find the delicate white flowers of Meadow Saxifrage *(Saxifraga granulata)* in springtime scattered among the buttercups. This is an elegant saxifrage with long flower stalks rising from pretty rounded leaves. A flower which is disappearing with the ploughing of permanent

PLATE 14
Greater Knapweed *(Centaurea scabiosa)* is common on open sites in mid summer.

pastures, this plant has noticeable bulbils which are formed in the angle between the stem and the stalk of the lower leaves. In this same grassland as snow in the grass, are the unfurling umbels of Pignut *(Conopodium majus)* and the showy flowers of Field Mouse Ear *(Cerastium arvense)*.

The limestone grassland often has a varied orchid population. Common Spotted Orchid *(Dactylorhiza fuchsii)* (Plate 7 on page 32) will be frequent and often Early Purple Orchid *(Orchis mascula)* will escape from the woodland to flower in the grass. Pyramid Orchid *(Anacamptis pyramidalis)* is frequent and flowers from early June until late August. This orchid is pollinated by day-flying butterflies in search of the nectar at the base of the long spur. During the evening the flower emits an unpleasant foxy smell which is intended to repel night-flying Lepidoptera in search of an evening meal. Hybridisation has been recorded between the Pyramid Orchid and the other candy pink orchid of the calcareous pasture, the Fragrant Orchid *(Gymnadenia conopsea)*. These two Orchids can easily be distinguished by inspecting the shape of the individual flowers. The lower lip of the Pyramid Orchid has two bosses at the entrance to the tube, whereas these are absent in Fragrant Orchid (Figure 3). The delightful scent of the Fragrant

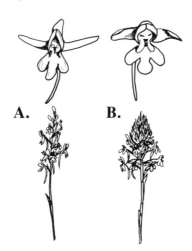

FIGURE 3   Two orchids of calcareous grassland. (A) Fragrant Orchid *(Gymnadenia conopsea)* and (B) Pyramid Orchid *(Anacamptis pyramidalis)*.

Orchid becomes rancid once pollination has occurred and this deters further insect visitors. As with all other orchids colour variations between different specimens can be extreme. It is not uncommon to find pure white Pyramid and Fragrant Orchids. It is not wise to try to identify orchids using colour as the main parameter. The pollination strategy of orchids never ceases to amaze. In these grasslands we can also find two flowers which show the ultimate in floral adaptation for this purpose, the mimicking orchids. The Fly Orchid *(Ophrys insectifera)* (Plate 16 on page 55) is probably more common at the woodland edge, and is mentioned in the chapter on limestone woodland. The Bee Orchid *(Ophrys apifera)* is intolerant of shade and prefers the sunlit oasis of the grassy bank between the trees. In the Park the Bee Orchid and the Fly Orchid are at the northernmost reaches of their distribution range, the former flowering from mid June and the latter from mid May. They can readily be distinguished from one another; the sepals behind the pseudo-insect petals are green in the Fly Orchid and pink in the Bee Orchid. These orchids are not always readily seen. The small dark flowers merge into the grassland and I have

PLATE 15
Wood Anemone *(Anemone nemorosa)* is frequent in both acid and alkaline woodlands.

53

seen many people walk past them without realising their presence. Most examples of this habitat were created by man and require the presence of man and his alien grazing animals if they are to survive. Shrub invasion can happen very quickly, with the loss of the most attractive light-loving flowers. When the grassland was first established after forest clearance, it was invaded by those members of the Late Glacial Flora which still persisted in neighbouring open limestone habitats, perhaps on crags or on soils too shallow or rocky for tree growth. These members of the Late Glacial Flora blossomed and multiplied in the open-grazed grassland. Thus even though the habitat itself is artificial, it has formed a refuge for an important element of our native wild flora and such a sanctuary is an extremely valuable habitat in the Park which must be conserved.

FACTS AND FICTION

Eyebright *(Euphrasia officinalis)*
The bright-eyed appearance of the flower encouraged herbalists to apply the Doctrine of Signatures and recommend the plant for clearing the eyesight. The 17th century botanist William Coles is reputed to have said that Linnets use the plant to clear the eyesight of their young. As short-sighted Linnets are hard to identify this theory has never been disproved! An extract of this plant is still used in an eye lotion.

Agrimony *(Agrimonia eupatoria)*
Named after the Greek King Mithradates Eupatoria 132–63 BC who was reputed to be the first person to discover its healing properties. Used for cataract of the eye, gout, bruised joints and is still used by ` herbalists in potions to cure liver complaints and aid digestion.

Lady's Mantle *(Alchemilla vulgaris* agg*)*
The common name likens the leaf shape to a lady's cloak. On the serrated margins of the leaves are glands which secrete water. This liquid often collects in the hollow of the leaf and was used by alchemists in their recipes for making gold. They called it celestial water.

PLATE 16
Fly Orchid *(Ophrys insectifera)* found in grassland and woodland along
the Corallian Limestone.

PLATE 17
Six Spot Burnet Moth *(Zygaena filipendulae)* on Spiny Rest Harrow *(Ononis spinosa)* at Runswick Bay.

56

CALCAREOUS WETLAND

Imagine a meadow crossed by a gentle stream rising crystal clear from limestone rocks. In springtime the brilliant shiny flowers of Marsh Marigold *(Caltha palustris)* line the brook, with the clear crisp pink Bird's Eye Primrose *(Primula farinosa)* clustered close by in the grass, and above them the delicate pink bells of Water Avens *(Geum rivale)*. In the hazy hot sunshine of a June day the air hangs still above the stream, Brooklime *(Veronica beccabunga)*, Watercress *(Nasturtium officinale)* and Tufted Forget-me-not *(Myosotis caespitosa)* root in the bed of the stream, whilst on the damp pasture beside the running water a profusion of Marsh and Spotted Orchids *(Dactylorhiza sp)*, and the opening buds of Fragrant Orchid *(Gymnadenia conopsea)* compete with each other for a place in the sun. In the short dusty days of late summer the meadow is tall and the air filled with dispersing seed. Meadowsweet *(Filipendula ulmaria)*, Hemp Agrimony *(Eupatorium cannabinum)*, Marsh Ragwort *(Senecio aquaticus)* and Great Hairy Willow Herb *(Epilobium hirsutum)* are conspicuous among the taller grasses, whilst in the shorter grassland dipping to the stream are the white flowers of Grass of Parnassus *(Parnassia palustris)*.

For the botanist the calcareous marsh is probably the most exciting habitat in the Park. In total, limestone wetlands cover a very small area, occurring as fragments of wet, stream-flushed meadow from Scarborough round the southern edge of the Moors to Black Hambleton. Most of the larger families of flowering plant are well represented in this habitat. Marsh Marigolds are the first buttercups to open their flowers in the spring and by June the smaller flowers of the Lesser Spearwort *(Ranunculus flammula)* accompany the fruiting heads of their larger relative. The Lesser Spearwort is in essence the water buttercup, easily distinguished from the meadowland buttercup by its linear leaves as compared with the complex leaves of the drier site buttercups which have several irregular leaflets (Figure 4). It is certainly true that Creeping

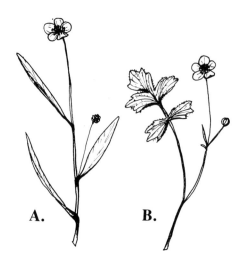

A. B.

FIGURE 4   Contrasting foliage of two buttercups found in the wet meadow.
(A) Lesser Spearwort *(Ranunculus flammula)* and (B) Creeping
Buttercup *(Ranunculus repens)*.

Buttercup *(Ranunculus repens)* will tolerate seasonally waterlogged soil and will be frequent in the wet meadow. The adapta-
bility of this buttercup is witnessed by its universal role as a
troublesome garden weed. In wetlands to the north of Pickering
you can find luxuriant growth of Globe Flowers *(Trollius
europaeus)*. This, the most attractive of all the buttercups, is the
lemon globe of cool climates and can be found far north into the
near arctic summer of northern Scotland.

Two closely related members of the cabbage family can be found
in this springtime marsh. Milkmaid *(Cardamine pratensis)* is
familiar to most lovers of the countryside; its delicate flowers open
early in the spring and can carpet the water meadow lilac. This
plant is one of the food plants for the caterpillar of the Orange Tip
Butterfly *(Anthocharis cardamines)*, one of the earliest emergent
butterflies, flying in June. The Large Bittercress *(Cardamine
amara)* is more unusual and can be distinguished from Milkmaid by
the white flowers, purple anthers and more robust foliage growth.

Flowering with these Cardamines is a pretty member of the pink
family (Caryophyllaceae), Ragged Robin *(Lychnis flos-cuculi)*
named from its pink ragged flowers. Individual flowers set seed
rapidly and quickly merge into the tangle of summer vegetation.

58

Water Avens and Meadowsweet are the only roses that grow happily on these wet alkaline soils, and flowering a deeper pink are the two willow herbs: Great Hairy, whose tall majestic stems are covered with a mass of large (2.5cm) flowers in August, and sheltered beneath them the inconspicuous Hoary Willow Herb *(Epilobium parviflorum)* which frequents the same habitat as its taller relative. While Fool's Water Cress *(Apium nodiflorum)* carries small dirty white umbels, hardly clear of the water of the stream, the robust Wild Angelica *(Angelica sylvestris)* waits until late July before large rounded umbel heads rise above the Meadowsweet blossoms. The foliage of Angelica is very attractive, a compound pinnate leaf which branches twice or thrice before it carries even-sized leaflets on narrowing stems; the whole leaf is very large and can extend to half a metre.

The Bird's Eye Primrose is the jewel of this habitat. The plant is much more common on the broad stretches of Carboniferous Limestone on the Pennines, but can still be found in equivalent calcareous habitats in the Park. The pink flowers with yellow throats open in late May and are borne in an umbel rising on a clear stalk from the mealy rosette of leaves. An alternative name is Mealy Primrose. The Grass of Parnassus is another very beautiful member of this community. The green fringed oil glands of the staminodes fan outward to the delicately veined petals giving the flower a fragile appearance (Plate 22). Close by, another pattern of veins on petals is seen in the Bog Pimpernel *(Anagallis tenella)* whose purple veins are etched in the pale pink flowers. This is a small plant whose leafy stems spread over the grass with numerous small rounded leaves.

Water Forget-me-nots can always be found by the streamside; sky blue against the reflective water they span a long flowering season as the individual buds on the many flowered raceme, open, fertilise and fruit through the long days of summer. A deeper blue along the stream will herald the presence of the ubiquitous Brooklime, a constant coloniser of the water edge. Brooklime is a little speedwell whose group belongs to the Snapdragon family (Scrophulariaceae). A larger red-flowered member of this same family is Red Rattle *(Pedicularis palustris)*. This plant is frequent on wet land and is partially parasitic on the roots of the surrounding grasses. The attractive purple-blue flowers of the insectivorous Butterwort *(Pinguicula vulgaris)* can often be found in the stream-

59

side wetland, the sticky leaves trapping any unwary springtime insect. Water Mint *(Mentha aquatica)* is the commonest member of the Mint family (Labiatae) that one will find; its aromatic leaves render the plant easy to recognise even before the appearance, in late summer of the interrupted spike of pale lilac flowers.

You can find two different Valerian in the wet meadow. Flowering in May, the smaller Marsh Valerian *(Valeriana dioica)* (about 30cm) always indicates a species rich habitat that will reward the plant hunter. By July the larger (often over a metre) Common Valerian *(Valeriana officinalis)* can also be found in slightly drier areas of the grassland. The pale pink flowers of these species are very similar, told apart firstly in stature but also by observing the lowest leaf pair on the stem. In Marsh Valerian the leaves are entire whereas in Common Valerian they are pinnately divided resembling the rest of the plant's foliage.

The Daisy family (Compositae) is a very large family with over a hundred common species. It is not surprising that this family is well represented in the marsh. The pink spikes of Butterbur *(Petasites hybridus)* push through the ground in the very early spring before the leaves are developed. After the fruiting head has disappeared the large rounded basal leaves seem to get larger and larger as the summer progresses; indeed many people call them Elephant Rhubarb. Male and female flowers occur on separate plants, and where the foliage is luxuriant most other vegetation is outshaded. Most members of the daisy family flower late in the summer: the yellow heads of Marsh Ragwort *(Senecio aquaticus)* and Fleabane *(Pulicaria dysenterica),* the pink rayless heads of Hemp Agrimony *(Eupatorium cannabinum)* and the tall purple stems of Marsh Thistle *(Cirsium palustre).* From the families of Monocotyledons the small Marsh Arrow Grass *(Triglochin palustre)* is common; the spiked inflorescence carries flowers without petals and consequently the plant is easily overlooked.

When the wet stream-side has been undisturbed for a long period the slow growing orchid flora may be very diverse. Marsh, Spotted and Fragrant Orchids *(Dactylorhiza sp. and Gymnadenia conopsea)* frequently hybridise and the resultant population of orchids will be highly individual, no two plants resembling each other in details of colour, lip marking or overall stature. A much rarer orchid of the marsh is the Marsh Helleborine *(Epipactis palustris)* which flowers later in the summer than the Marsh Orchids, from mid July onwards.

This is a most attractive pink-purple-white flowered orchid with large flowers (2cm) and the plant can still be found in wetlands near Helmsley.

Species which regularly occur in the marsh (excluding grasses):—

Marsh Marigold	*Caltha palustris*
Milkmaid	*Cardamine pratensis*
Ragged Robin	*Lychnis flos-cuculi*
Water Avens	*Geum rivale*
Meadowsweet	*Filipendula ulmaria*
Angelica	*Angelica sylvestris*
Fool's Water Cress	*Apium nodiflorum*
Bird's Eye Primrose	*Primula farinosa*
Water Forget-me-not	*Myosotis scorpioides*
Red Rattle	*Pedicularis palustris*
Brooklime	*Veronica beccabunga*
Water Cress	*Nasturtium officinale*
Marsh Valerian	*Valeriana dioica*
Marsh Ragwort	*Senecio aquaticus*
Bog Pimpernel	*Anagallis tenella*
Grass of Parnassus	*Parnassia palustris*
Hemp Agrimony	*Eupatorium cannabinum*
Marsh Thistle	*Cirsium palustre*
Marsh Arrow Grass	*Triglochin palustris*
Early Marsh Orchid	*Dactylorhiza incarnata*
Northern Marsh Orchid	*D. purpurella*
Common Spotted Orchid	*D. fuchsii*
Fragrant Orchid	*Gymnadenia conopsea*
Hairy Sedge	*Carex hirta*
Lesser Pond Sedge	*C. acutiformis*
Yellow Sedge group	*C. demissa*
Hard Rush	*Juncus inflexus*
Jointed Rush	*Juncus articulatus*

The wet meadow is a prime site for the sedge enthusiast: Lesser Pond Sedge *(Carex acutiformis)* by the waterside leading to the Yellow Sedges *(Carex demissa* group*)*, Hairy Sedge *(Carex hirta)*, Common Sedge *(Carex nigra)* and many other rarer sedges, all growing vigorously in the water-charged turf.

It is well to remember that this is one of the most fragile habitats of the Park. A certain level of grazing is essential to prevent shrub invasion into the drier parts of the meadow. Water-charged vegetation is very intolerant of trampling, and whether this is by naturalist, rambler or grazing stock is immaterial to the plants. In all cases the effect can be devastating. Fortunately two important meadows are managed as reserves by the Yorkshire Wildlife Trust, Hagg Wood near Lockton and Ashberry Pasture near Helmsley.

The wet meadows described here are one of my favourite haunts. The mixed community of plants of the meadow has a long flowering season. As the tedious flower-less winter drags on I look to the first days in March for the brilliant yellow of the Marsh Marigold casting its glow across the dormant meadow, and in the autumn when golds and browns signal the approach of the winter sleep I can still find a purple of Great Hairy Willow Herb, or Marsh Thistle and a white of the beautiful Grass of Parnassus (Plate 22). The number of different species in a small area is very large; most are very attractive, many are local or rare.

Gormire Lake is the only natural body of open water in the Park. This is an ancient habitat with a rich and interesting flora that includes several rare species. Gormire is an area of ancient legend, of horse and rider that jumped from the Whitestone Cliff to be lost forever in the lake and the popular belief that the lake plumbed bottomless depths. Although the lake water is low in nutrients the banks have a rich vegetation:—

Gypsywort	*Lycopus europaeus*
Marsh Cinquefoil	*Potentilla palustris*
Bog Bean	*Menyanthes trifoliata*
Great Hairy Willow Herb	*Epilobium hirsutum*
Flag	*Iris pseudacorus*
Common Spotted Orchid	*Dactylorhiza fuchsii*
Water Plantain	*Alisma plantago-aquatica*
Marsh Pennywort	*Hydrocotyle vulgaris*

The lake adjoins the Yorkshire Wildlife Trust reserve of Garbutt Wood whose wooded slopes climb to the open calcareous vegetation of the cliff itself. The Cleveland Way crosses along the top of the cliff giving both a good view of, and access to, both the woodland and the lake below.

FACTS AND FICTION

Lesser Spearwort *(Ranunculus flammula)*
The specific name likens the leaf shape to a flame, and the generic name refers to Rana the latin for a frog indicating that like the Spearwort many of this genera inhabit wet places. The juice of the plant is very acid; traditionally beggars used the juice to cause skin sores, and gain sympathy from passers by.

Milkmaid *(Cardamine pratensis)*
A common flower with many local names including Cuckoo Flower, Ladies Smock. All the Cardamines have edible leaves which taste rather like Water Cress and are rich in Vitamin C. In time past the plant was said to strengthen a weak heart, hence the generic name. The flower was said to belong to the fairies and it was thought unlucky to bring it into the home. The plant often has cuckoo-spit on its foliage, formed by leaf hoppers that suck the juice from the stem. When this juice is exposed to air it becomes frothy.

Hemp Agrimony *(Eupatorium cannabinum)*
This plant was named after King Mithradates Eupatoria from Greece who was reputed to be the first to recognise the medicinal use of the plant as a cure for jaundice and to 'cleanse' the bladder and kidney. The leaves of the plant are superficially like those of Hemp, being one of the few members of the Daisy family that have opposite leaves.

Water Forget-me-not *(Myosotis scorpioides)*
The forget-me-nots were traditionally named from the German legend of the knight who walked beside a deep river with his new bride. He stooped down to pick a flower for his wife, fell in and was swept away. Tossing the flowers to his love he called forget-me-not. These flowers were also once called Scorpion Grass from the coil that the spike of buds forms as it unfolds.

PLATE 18
Runswick Bay from the Kettleness alum workings.

COASTLINE

The coastline of the Park is exceptionally beautiful, predominantly high cliffs falling dramatically to the restless and treacherous North Sea. The Cleveland Way follows the whole of this stretch of coastline providing good access on well marked routes on 25 miles of pathway. Although many streams find their way to the sea along this coastline, most of the rain falls on the high ground of the Moors, flows west and south and eventually reaches the Humber Estuary via the Derwent River. The Derwent itself rises deep within the Park in the lonely reaches of Lilla Howe. In many areas the cliffs are cut by steep valleys carved by stream erosion as the waters force their way to the sea. The Thorny Beck winds through the wooded ravines of Staintondale before the waters drop down a short waterfall to the beach at Hayburn Wyke. The area is included in the Yorkshire Wildlife Trust Reserve of the same name. A little to the north, Stoup Beck and Mill Beck flow into the sea in Robin Hood's Bay, and at Runswick Bay (Plate 18) several streams pass through wooded dales before they reach the sandy bay. A multitude of streams coalesce in the extensive woodland tract at Mulgrave, eventually flowing across the beach at Sandsend. The waters of the River Esk have had the most dramatic effect on the cliff coastline now cutting a wide channel through the busy tourist resort and fishing town of Whitby.

In many places the cliffs themselves do not fall perpendicular to the sea but by a series of shelves or cliff slips. The most notable area of slip is at Beast Cliff. Here the higher cliffs are very steep and have ancient scrub woodland dominated by Hawthorn *(Crataegus monogyna)*, Mountain Ash *(Sorbus aucuparia)*, Birch *(Betula* sp.*)* and Blackthorn *(Prunus spinosa)*. Below this cliff a large lush plateau shows a wide range of habitat types, from woodland dominated by Oak *(Quercus petraea)* and Ash *(Fraxinus excelsior)*, areas thick with Bracken *(Pteridium aquilinum)* and calcareous outcrops dominated by Rock Rose *(Helianthemum chamaecistus)*, Quaking

Grass *(Briza media)*, and Salad Burnet *(Poterium sanguisorba)*. There is also wetland vegetation around the margins of a number of ponds.

Areas of mixed woodland on this plateau have been little disturbed by man, their inaccessibility precluding woodland management. The dense shady woodland boasts a rich fern flora:—

Male Fern	*Dryopteris filix-mas*
Broad Buckler Fern	*D. dilitata*
Lady Fern	*Athyrium filix-femina*
Soft Shield Fern	*Polystichum setiferum*
Common Polypody	*Polypodium vulgare*
Hart's Tongue Fern	*Phyllitis scolopendrium*

The flora of the cliff ledges is often well above the influence of sea spray; consequently maritime vegetation is not well developed along this high cliff coast. Seaside plants which can be found include the ubiquitous Sea Plantain *(Plantago maritima)* Scurvy Grass *(Cochlearia officinalis)* and Sea Wormwood *(Artemisia maritima)* with Sea Milkwort *(Glaux maritima)* on occasional saline depressions.

Seepage through the rock strata of the cliffs often creates fresh water flushes which have a rich flora. Grass of Parnassus *(Parnassia palustis)* (Plate 22) and Northern Marsh Orchids *(Dactylorhiza purpurella)* will be frequent in this habitat.

Species typical of wet areas:—

Northern Marsh Orchid	*Dactylorhiza purpurella*
Grass of Parnassus	*Parnassia palustris*
Water Mint	*Mentha aquatica*
Brooklime	*Veronica beccabunga*
Giant Horsetail	*Equisetum telmateia*
Ragged Robin	*Lychnis flos-cuculi*
Fleabane	*Pulicaria dysenterica*
Hard Rush	*Juncus inflexus*
Marsh Thistle	*Cirsium palustre*
Great Hairy Willow Herb	*Epilobium hirsutum*
Hemp Agrimony	*Eupatorium cannabinum*

Hard Rush *(Juncus inflexus)* can be differentiated from Common

66

Rush *(Juncus effusus)* by examination of the white pith lining the centre of the stem. In Hard Rush this pith is interrupted giving the appearance of a step ladder, whereas in Common Rush the pith forms a continuous white sheet along the whole length of the stem. The grassland of the drier cliffs often shows a calcareous flora. Near Ravenscar such grassland has a rich orchid flora. The early flowering Early Purple Orchids *(Orchis mascula)* are followed by Pyramid Orchid *(Anacamptis pyramidalis)*, Fragrant Orchid *(Gymnadenia conopsea)* and Frog Orchid *(Coeloglossum viride)*. Distinguishing features between Pyramid and Fragrant Orchids are shown in Figure 3. Frog Orchid is both uncommon and difficult to see, the green flowers blending in with the shades of grassland. The shape of each flower resembles a jumping frog and the whole spike doesn't usually exceed 15cm in height. This orchid is very versatile in its habitat tolerance and will venture higher than any other orchid, along the mountain ledges of Northern Europe.

Other species of the dry calcareous cliff:—

Yellow Rattle	*Rhinanthus minor*
Kidney Vetch	*Anthyllis vulneraria*
Bird's Foot Trefoil	*Lotus corniculatus*
Quaking Grass	*Briza media*
Salad Burnet	*Poterium sanguisorba*
Glaucous sedge	*Carex flacca*
Common Milkwort	*Polygala vulgaris*
Carline Thistle	*Carlina vulgaris*

The greater part of the cliffs are over acid bedrock and have a flora which is very similar to that of the drier moorlands. Great Woodrush *(Luzula sylvatica)*, Wood Sage *(Teucrium scorodonia)* and Golden Rod *(Solidago virgaurea)* are more common on the sea cliff than inland. Indeed these three plants are regular members of the acid cliff communities around the length of Northern Britain.

Other important species of the acid cliffs:—

Heather	*Calluna vulgaris*
Bell Heather	*Erica cinerea*
Crowberry	*Empetrum nigrum*
Bilberry	*Vaccinium myrtillus*
Bracken	*Pteridium aquilinum*
Beautiful St. John's Wort	*Hypericum pulchrum*

PLATE 19
Wood Vetch *(Vicia sylvatica)* is common along the sea cliffs.

68

Perhaps one of the most notable flowers of this coastline is Wood Vetch *(Vicia sylvatica)* shown in Plate 19. Locally common on the cliffs the beautiful flowers are a delightful feature of this attractive landscape. The size and arrangement of the flowers are similar to the common hedgerow vetch Tufted Vetch *(Vicia cracca)*. In contrast with the deep purple-blue flowers of the latter, Wood Vetch has delicate pale lilac petals which are decorated by dark purple veins. I have seen the Wood Vetch along several stretches of the Park coastline but nowhere so profuse as beneath the little village of Kettleness where Herring Gulls soar over boulders and cliff banks are covered in a profusion of these delicately coloured flowers.

FACTS AND FICTION

Scurvy Grass *(Cochlearia officinalis)*
This genus of plants was named after cochlea, the shell of a snail. The succulent rounded leaves were thought to resemble a shell. The foliage is rich in vitamin C and since it grows all around our coastline was easily available for sailors to eat, and combat the deficiency disease of scurvy. The flowers and leaves have also been used as a tonic and to arrest nose bleeds.

Grass of Parnassus *(Parnassia palustris)*
This flower was described and named in Greece 2,000 years ago by Dioscorides. He was one of the first eminent botanists and sought plants primarily for their medicinal uses. He was a physician to the Roman army and travelled extensively around the Mediterranean. The flower will grow up to 2,600 ft on our mountains, always being found in wet flushes (Plate 22).

Golden Rod *(Solidago virgaurea)*
The generic name comes from the Latin *solidare* to heal, reflecting the long-term belief in the plant's healing powers. A tea made from the leaves is reputed to improve digestion and help to cure tuberculosis and bronchitis. The plant was also applied externally to heal wounds.

THE LONG VALLEYS

On the southern edge of the Park, the great valleys of Bilsdale, Bransdale, Farndale and Rosedale stretch deep into the flat-topped moorland. In these valleys the limestone belt pushes a long tongue into the moorland plateau. These are ancient valleys which precede the last Ice Age and show a mixed land use with remnants of natural woodland, arable crop, Forestry Commission plantation and riverside pasture.

The most notable of these valleys is Farndale, owing much of its fame to the profusion of Wild Daffodils *(Narcissus pseudonarcissus)* along the wet meadows and woodland edge beside the river Dove. These Wild Daffodils are a magnificent sight in late April, protected in a local nature reserve where public footpaths by the river give good access to the main daffodil area. Daffodils growing along the river bank are shown in Plate 20. The

PLATE 20
Wild Daffodils *(Narcissus pseudonarcissus)* along the river Dove.

70

Wild Daffodil is more commonly found in southern and more western parts of Britain. The distribution of the daffodil in the Park is not restricted to Farndale. In his book on North Yorkshire, J. G. Baker (1863), had records of it from Goathland Dale, Eskdale, Harwood Dale, Yedmandale and near Scarborough, and at the present time the Wild Daffodil is conspicuous in the valleys adjacent to Farndale. Flowering along with the daffodils in the woodside remnants along the Dove you can also find the more familiar flowers of springtime:—

Opposite Leaved Golden Saxifrage	*Chrysosplenium oppositifolia*
Lesser Celandine	*Ranunculus ficaria*
Wood Anemone	*Anemone nemorosa*
Town Hall Clock	*Adoxa moschatellina*
Cuckoo Pint	*Arum maculatum*
Wild Garlic	*Allium ursinum*
Primrose	*Primula vulgaris*
Barren Strawberry	*Potentilla sterilis*

Town Hall Clock *(Adoxa moschatellina)* is a small flower which is easily overlooked by the rambler. The small spherical flower head with five flowers, four around the circumference and one on top, is also called Five-Faced Bishop. The yellow-green flower head appears in April sprouting from delicately lobed foliage which is not unlike that of Wood Anemone. Town Hall Clock is illustrated in Plate 21.

The Heather *(Calluna vulgaris)* clad Moorland is never far from these valley bottoms, skirting the tops of the valley sides, looking down on a rural landscape of village and field boundary.

Bransdale grades quickly to moorland in its upper reaches, but in total gives a wide range of habitats to explore (Plate 6). In early summer the hedgerow will be white with Cow Parsley *(Anthriscus sylvestris)* or the more attractive frothy cream umbels of Sweet Cicely *(Myrrhis odorata)*. The foliage and long seeds of Sweet Cicely smell strongly of aniseed and have been used by country people in cooking and to scent furniture polish. In June the close-cropped roadside verge is purple with Thyme *(Thymus drucei)* and white with Eyebright *(Euphrasia officinalis)*. Later in the summer these same shades will witness Felwort *(Gentianella amarella)* and Knotted Pearlwort *(Sagina nodosa)*. As the road dips to a stream

PLATE 21
Town Hall Clock *(Adoxa moschatellina)* is an elusive woodland flower
of the early spring.

the wet pasture of late summer will be purple with Great Hairy
Willow Herb *(Epilobium hirsutum)* and Hoary Willow Herb
(Epilobium parviflorum) and white with Grass of Parnassus
(Parnassia palustris) Plate 22. Passing Forestry Commission
plantation and moorland edge you may find the pink flowers of
Pink Purslane *(Montia sibirica)* in lowland roadside pasture.
  Valley sides in Bilsdale will be springtime blue with Bluebell
(Hyacinthoides non-scripta) on slopes that later in the year are
dominated by Bracken *(Pteridium aquilinum)*, or sheep-grazed
pastures with a good mixture of herbs:—

Bitter Vetch	*Lathyrus montanus*
Self-Heal	*Prunella vulgaris*
Common Sorrel	*Rumex acetosella*
Bulbous buttercup	*Ranunculus bulbosus*
Common Cat's Ear	*Hypochoeris radicata*
Sneezewort	*Achillea ptarmica*
Marsh Thistle	*Cirsium palustre*
Pignut	*Conopodium majus*

72

Lady's Mantle	*Alchemilla sp.*
Red Bartsia	*Odontites verna*

Newtondale is a spectacular deep-sided valley that runs south from high on the Moors at Fen Bog to reach the Vale of Pickering. This is a recent valley gouged out by melt-waters overflowing from Lake Esk at the end of the last Ice Age. This flat-bottomed valley was chosen as the natural course of the railway from Pickering to Whitby, designed by George Stephenson in 1836 and finally closed by British Rail in 1965. Reopened in 1967 as the North Yorkshire Moors Railway the line gives unparalleled views of the North Yorkshire Moors.

In many areas in Newtondale calcareous water from the limestone band enriches the wetland vegetation to give species rich marsh and wet pasture. Fen Bog at the head of Newtondale is a Yorkshire Wildlife Trust Reserve. Historically the ground water supply to this bog was modified when the railway was built on rafts across the depression which outlines the bog. Sections of the bog are now influenced by acid nutrient-poor run off from surrounding sandstone and show a typical bog vegetation. At the southern end of the bog, influence from calcareous rocks is greater and fen vegetation adds to the total diversity of the bog. Fen Bog is aptly named since in the vegetational sequence from bog to fen it has been shown that Fen Bog lies midway between the two extremes. Hagg Wood Marsh lies at the junction of Newtondale with a narrow valley running under Lockton. This is a Yorkshire Wildlife Trust Reserve with a very rich calcareous flora.

Meadows alongside the railway have a lush tall vegetation which will include Marsh Thistle *(Cirsium palustre)*, Marsh Ragwort *(Senecio aquatious)* and Common Valerian *(Valeriana officinalis).* By the edges of the streams the pretty flowers of Purple Loosestrife *(Lythrum salicaria)* and Common Skullcap *(Scutellaria galericulata)* will flourish in the wet rich soil. Along the Forestry Commission tracks the illuminated verge will show a much more interesting display of flowers than can be found in the deep dark plantations themselves. The woodland floor under the dense monoculture of alien coniferous trees is a perpetually dark environment in which very few flowering plants can survive.

By the roadside the shrubs of Broom *(Cytisus scoparius)* and Gorse *(Ulex europaeus)* are common, as are the wild roses. Dog

Rose *(Rosa canina)* will occur most frequently, but in Newtondale you can find Field Rose *(Rosa arvensis)*. The key to identification lies in the centre of the flower; in Field Rose the styles are united to form a chimney which projects from the centre of the flower to overtop the numerous stamens. These two roses are illustrated in Figure 5.

Through its length Newtondale shows wide ranging habitats which mirror the variety of landscapes to be found across the whole of the inland areas of the Park. Forestry plantations, fragments of ancient woodland, dry moorland crags and rich streamside vegetation are all to be found in this valley.

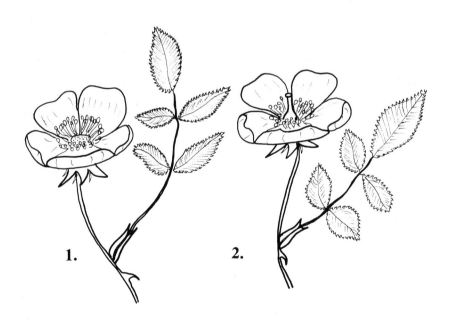

FIGURE 5   Contrasting flower shapes of 1. Dog Rose *(Rosa canina)* and 2. Field Rose *(Rosa arvensis)*.

FACTS AND FICTION

Wild Daffodil *(Narcissus pseudonarcissus)*
In Britain this wild flower only occurs in England and Wales. Also called the Lent Lily from its flowering time at Easter. Although much commoner in western parts of the country, the massed blooms of Farndale are a famous tourist attraction. The bulb has narcotic properties and in small doses is a purgative and emetic.

Pink Purslane *(Montia sibirica)*
This is a recent introduction into the country from North America. Seeds are thought to have come in with cotton brought along the Manchester Ship Canal. Certainly now this pretty pink flower can be found from northern Scotland to Cornwall.

Bitter Vetch *(Lathyrus montanus)*
The common name can be criticised since the plant is a pea rather than a vetch, and the Latin name because although *montanus* refers to mountains the flower rather favours upland pastures. The flower has red buds which open to purple flowers, probably in response to a change in the acidity of the cell sap rather like litmus paper. The tubers of the plant have been used as a vegetable crop since the Middle Ages. The raw tubers taste like chestnut and were tied in bundles and hung under the thatch to dry. They were also used to flavour whisky.

ARTIFICIAL HABITATS

The role of man in the landscape began many centuries ago and every habitat has felt his influence. His activities were not restricted to tree felling, growth of arable crops and grazing stock. Over the years his pastimes have been extremely varied. He has quarried the natural stone from the hillside to supply building materials; for the powerful: to build their great castles; for the religious and powerful: their churches and monasteries; and for the peasantry: farmhouse, sheep-fold and dry stone wall. Many of these quarries have since been abandoned. Quarrying has exposed cliffs of sandstone or limestone and, free from grazing pressure or man's interest, these exposed rock outcrops have been colonised by the plants typical of these Jurassic rocks.

The sandstone crag will support Golden Rod *(Solidago virgaurea)*, Wall Lettuce *(Mycelis muralis)*, Wood Sage *(Teucrium scorodonia)* and Foxglove *(Digitalis purpurea)* along with species typical of the driest heathland, Bell Heather *(Erica cinerea)* and Bilberry *(Vaccinium myrtillus)*.

The limestone quarry has a richer flora. The pockets of soil on high ledges can support any of the communities of flowers previously described for dry limestone grasslands. Tolerance of drought will be even more important in this habitat than in the grassland. Deep-rooted flowers such as Salad Burnet *(Poterium sanguisorba)* and Thyme *(Thymus drucei)* may tap sources of moisture unavailable to their competitors. Waxy leaves will resist water loss and their possession gives Rock Rose *(Helianthemum chamaecistus)* an advantage over any delicately leaved neighbours.

If we follow the skilled masons to their monumental achievements in limestone and sandstone, to castle and abbey we will find a fascinating array of wild flowers. Long since ruined and derelict, abandoned to Jackdaw and Rabbit, the ancient monuments of the Park are now carefully preserved and tended. The enthusiasm of the gardener to trim and weed relates directly to the wild flower flora to be found in his domain. The Cistercian Monastery at Byland Abbey has been carefully manicured, but even here the high towers are dotted with blue as clumps of Harebell *(Campanula rotundifolia)* wave in the breeze. Earlier in the season the tops of the lower walls have numerous Three-Fingered Saxifrage *(Saxifraga tridactylites)* and Thale Cress *(Arabidopsis thaliana)*. Both have tiny white flowers but the Saxifrage has five petals and stems and leaves which turn red as they dry and can be recognised throughout the late summer as the fruit ripens. Thale Cress is a diminutive member of the Cabbage family with four petals and long thin fruits. Whitlow Grass *(Erophila verna)* is in the same family and flowers very early on the old ruins, even at Easter time when the spring is sunny and kind. The notched petals of Whitlow Grass are distinctive, and salient features to separate the two are shown in Figure 6.

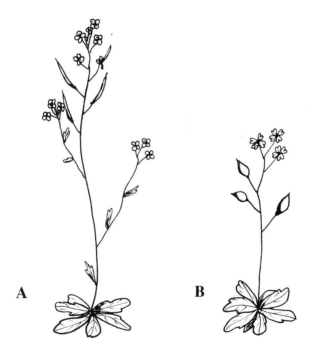

FIGURE 6   Two springtime members of the cabbage family that you frequently find on old ruins. (A) Thale Cress *(Arabidopsis thaliana)* and (B) Whitlow Grass *(Erophila verna)*.

Helmsley Castle grounds display a fabulous array of wild flowers. The outer defences of the castle are two ditches separated by a steep sided earthwork. Parts of the embankment are not regularly mown and in August give a breathtaking view of Musk Mallow *(Malva moschata)* and Marjoram *(Origanum vulgare)*. Both these limestone plants are present in white- and pink-flowered form and bear witness to a well planned landscaping regime which combines conservation interests with tidiness. In June the walls themselves are pink with the introduced alpine Fairy Foxglove *(Erinus alpinus)*, familiar both to rock garden enthusiasts and anyone who has climbed Continental mountains in search of flowers. Coupled with the blue of Viper's Bugloss *(Echium vulgare)* and the yellow Ragwort *(Senecio jacobea)* the old walls are alive with colour. I recorded 84 different vascular plants in July 1985. On the western cliffs of the castle walls the purple flowers of Black Horehound *(Ballota nigra)*, Common Mallow *(Malva sylvestris)* and Black Knapweed *(Centaurea nigra)* mingle together in profusion perched high above the deep ditch. The castle offers as much to the botanist as the historian.

Mount Grace Priory is one of the best preserved Carthusian Monasteries in the country. Built of sandstone the flora of the walls and grounds gives an interesting mixture of acid-loving and alkaline-preferring plants. English Stonecrop *(Sedum anglicum)*, Foxglove and Great Woodrush *(Luzula sylvatica)*, so familiar from acid hill or coastline, grow near Mullein *(Verbascum thapsus)*, Hairy St. John's Wort *(Hypericum hirsutum)* and Weld *(Reseda lutea)* which are plants reminiscent of the limestone country to the south. The solitary monks of this order each tended their own garden and the present flora could well reflect the activity of these ancient monks, where gardening ceased when the monastery was closed in 1539. Or one can conjecture that the green dye extracted from Weld was used to colour garments, the seeds from Mullein put among their clothes to keep away moths and the extracts from the St. John's Wort used as a mediaeval antiseptic.

It would be misleading to present a list of typical species to be found on old ruins. The flora of each site reflects the history of the building, the time of dereliction, the stone from which it was built and recent management aims. However on any of the ruins in the National Park you are likely to meet:—

78

PLATE 22
Grass of Parnassus *(Parnassia palustris)* the late flowering jewel
of the calcareous flush.

79

PLATE 23
Robin Hood's Bay with Common Cat's Ear *(Hypochoeris radicata)*
in the foreground.

Annual Pearlwort	*Sagina apetala*
Three-Fingered Saxifrage	*Saxifraga tridactylites*
Harebell	*Campanula rotundifolia*
Ivy	*Hedera helix*
Wall Lettuce	*Mycelis muralis*
Thyme Leaved Sandwort	*Arenaria serpyllifolia*
Wall Speedwell	*Veronica arvensis*

Quarrying activities on the Moors were not simply for building materials. The development of Middlesbrough as a large town followed the discovery of ironstone in the Cleveland Hills. From the 17th century for three hundred years, extraction of alum from shale represented another major industry on the Moors. The scars and evidence of these industries are frequent across the Park from the very shape of Roseberry Topping's collapsed peak to the bare shale tips below Kettleness. Iron and aluminium are amongst the most poisonous chemicals to plant growth in acid soils. It is not surprising that such abandoned quarries and waste heaps are not particularly exciting for discovering wild flowers. The long period since such sites have been used is witnessed by the profusion of slow-growing heaths *(Calluna vulgaris* and *Erica cinerea)*. Extraction industries have waxed and waned on the Moors. After the closure of the alum workings several places developed alternative industries to employ local labour and in their turn some of these have been closed down or curtailed. The old brick works at Grosmont left workings and tips which have long since been abandoned to colonisation by scrub woodland and grassland. Finding a richer soil source for growth than on a sandstone quarry or shale heap, herbaceous plants grow here in abundance.

Ox Eye Daisy	*Chrysanthemum leucanthemum*
Barren Strawberry	*Potentilla sterilis*
Primrose	*Primula vulgaris*
Meadow Vetchling	*Lathyrus pratensis*
Common St. John's Wort	*Hypericum perforatum*
Bush Vetch	*Vicia sepium*
Common Vetch	*Vicia sativa*
Black Knapweed	*Centaurea nigra*
Hairy Tare	*Vicia hirsuta*
Rough Hawkbit	*Leontodon hispidus*

81

Bird's Foot Trefoil	*Lotus corniculatus*
Common Spotted Orchid	*Dactylorhiza fuchsii*
Common Twayblade	*Listera ovata*
Broad-Leaved Helleborine	*Epipactis helleborine*

Derelict buildings will be colonised by both Yellow Stonecrop *(Sedum acre)* and English Stonecrop. The presence of orchids will always indicate that a site has been left undisturbed for a considerable period. The orchid seedling will usually take six years or more to develop the vegetative growth which must precede flower initiation.

Earth movements and disturbance of the soil will often create new and interesting habitats. If the soil is brought in from distant localities it may contain seeds of plants which were not previously present in the neighbourhood flora. If the soil is overturned buried weed seeds can be brought up to the surface to find an environment favourable for germination. We are all familiar with the flush of Field Poppies *(Papaver rhoeas)* on the banks of new roads. The tortuous descent to Runswick Bay has been replaced by a new road that cuts into a hillside which is artificially stabilised and drained. A profusion of different wild flowers colonise these banks. As springtime moves into summer the pale yellow umbels of Kidney Vetch *(Anthyllis vulneraria)* are replaced by a mass of pink flowers which carpet the bank. This is the blossom and thorny foliage of Spiny Restharrow *(Ononis spinosa)* illustrated in Plate 17. With flowers and leaves very reminiscent of its more common relative Restharrow *(Ononis repens)* the two can be told apart instantly and possibly painfully when the stems and foliage are grasped in the hand.

In midsummer among the short grass the Common Centaury *(Centaurium erythraea)* is frequent. This plant also has pink flowers but is of more delicate growth form than the robust Restharrow. Yellows and pinks dominate the wild flowers of this bank. Bird's Foot Trefoil *(Lotus corniculatus)* is common, a ready food plant for the caterpillars of the 6-spot Burnet Moth. The adult moth is shown in Plate 17 resting on the Spiny Restharrow. The presence of Wild Carrot *(Daucus carota)* on the roadside bank will remind the naturalist that he is near the sea and encourage him to turn and admire the view across the Bay to the towering cliffs of Kettleness, grey and gaunt with shale tips. The long-disused coastal railway line is another memento of the past, belonging to a time when the coastal resorts were teeming with holiday-makers who reached their seaside Mecca in the carriages of steam trains. The family car sounded the death knell of the branch line just as surely as the package holiday to the warm Mediterranean gave an alternative to the eternally cold waters of the North Sea. The disused railway from Scarborough to Staithes offers marvellous pedestrian access to unspoilt countryside. Floristically this line is not so exciting as the disused lines of the Yorkshire Wolds to the south where the track often cuts deep into the chalk bedrock providing a cliff refuge for the beautiful chalk flora.

As man leaves castle, quarry and railway behind, the wild flora follows close on his heels. Most artificial habitats will very quickly become a playground for common wild flowers. With the passing of time the seeds of rarer plants will begin to arrive. The resulting habitat can become a rich and wild refuge for our native flora.

FACTS AND FICTION

Whitlow Grass *(Erophila verna)*
Infusions of this tiny plant were once used to treat whitlows. Surprising perhaps, but an even more unlikely cure for this finger inflammation was a poultice of chewed bread. This is an ancient common name, the epithet 'grass' deriving from the word green. In olden days many flowers were called grass simply because they were green plants.

Black Horehound *(Ballota nigra)*
This plant was the old cure for rabies. Dating back to Greek times, the leaves were beaten with salt and applied to infected bites. The plant has a rather revolting smell.

Common Mallow *(Malva sylvestris)*
This is an important medicinal plant which was used as a soothing agent against inflammation of all kinds, from the eyes to the gastric system. Chewing the fresh flowers was reputed to relieve toothache and when crushed with olive oil gave relief to bee and wasp stings. The leaves can be cooked like spinach; one interesting recipe recommends frying in batter.

Wild Carrot *(Daucus carota)*
As would be expected from this wild ancestor of our 'domesticated' carrot the root is rich in vitamins. The plant has been used medicinally to cure diarrhoea and expel intestinal worms. The most popular use of the pulped root is as a soothing agent to relieve itching due to insect bites or eczema.

CONSERVATION

The title of this chapter is a single word with a wide ranging meaning, open to many interpretations. I take the question for the chapter to be: How can we best foster and encourage the natural history of the North Yorkshire Moors? Many bodies are active in this respect: the National Park Committee itself, North Yorkshire County Council, the National Trust, the Yorkshire Wildlife Trust and the Nature Conservancy. The last manages the National Nature Reserve at Forge Valley and is the consultative body for the management of the numerous national and local grade Sites of Special Scientific Interest (S.S.S.I.) which dot the Park. Across the country as a whole there are over 4,000 sites which are designated by the Nature Conservancy as S.S.S.I., and they represent a cross-section of all British habitat types. S.S.S.I.'s remain under the control of the occupier of the land and the Nature Conservancy acts as technical adviser particularly when any change of land use is projected.

It is important to realise that S.S.S.I.'s represent a sample of biologically important sites rather than the sum of valuable sites. Nature Conservancy surveys show that S.S.S.I.'s are still being damaged by their occupiers at a frightening rate; for example in the year 1980, 10–15% of S.S.S.I.'s across the country suffered significant damage (Moore). The Conservancy has also shown that the major cause of damage is agricultural activity. If sites which have planning protection are suffering such damage, it is clear that the deterioration of unprotected natural habitats is a major problem. The practices which are most likely to change the *status quo* of semi-natural habitats such as pasture, wetland or heathland are drainage schemes, herbicide use, fertiliser treatment, ploughing, reseeding and overgrazing.

Before we decry a landowner for trying to increase the profitability of his land we should reflect that rejection of available modern technology in favour of protecting the natural

85

wild environment will almost inevitably cost the landowner money. How many of us would donate the same percentage of our hard earned income to this same cause? The percentage of the Park protected as Reserve or S.S.S.I. is very small. The vastly greater area of the Park is managed commercially for forestry, farming or as grouse moor. Conservation targets for such a large and varied landscape must be designed around a basic factual framework:—

1. Landowners expect an income from management of their land, whether this be from forestry or farming.
2. The livelihood of many people living in the Park is based on the success of the landowner in achieving this end.
3. Tourism is both an important industry and a growth industry on the Moors.
4. As public leisure time increases more and more people will visit the Park for recreation.
5. Walking is becoming an increasingly popular pastime and use of public footpaths will increase.

Conservation begins when a landowner accepts the value of natural communities on his land and seeks to achieve a balance between his financial aspirations and his moral obligation to protect a part of our national heritage. It is clear that the landowner must be made aware of the natural history interest which is included in his land, whether it is an S.S.S.I. or not. In these days of intensive land use the role of the secretive naturalist is disappearing. A rare plant is not safe simply because only a handful of people know of its existence. The owner of the land should also be made aware. So often such knowledge leads to interest and even enthusiasm and the dedicated naturalist must seek to spread such excitement like an infectious disease. Conservation continues, when for a given site the wish to protect the natural environment outweighs any profit motive. Management of a site by a conservation body either through leasehold arrangement or outright ownership is a certain way to achieve these ends. An interesting, exciting habitat will often come under a dual management interest, e.g. Ashberry Pasture is a Yorkshire Wildlife Trust Reserve but also warrants designation as an S.S.S.I. and therefore attracts obligatory Nature Conservancy interest. The numerous reserves on the moors are listed on page 93. It is incorrect to assume that all these habitats are

86

PLATE 24
View from Carlton Bank just north of Helmsley.

protected for all time. Many of the Yorkshire Wildlife Trust Reserves are managed on long-term lease and are not owned outright.

Designation of a habitat as a reserve is not the end of the conservation story but the beginning of a continuing serial. Management control is the necessary precursor to the management plan, but each type of reserve has its own inherent problems. An expressed aim of any management strategy will be to maintain the species diversity present in the reserve.

Let us first examine management of the heathland itself. Under the climate of the North Yorkshire Moors the natural vegetation is deciduous woodland. Since the removal of this woodland by ancient man, the high moorland soils have become depleted of nutrients by centuries of rainfall washing minerals through the porous sandstone soils. Heather *(Calluna vulgaris)* is well adapted to this habitat and the expansive moorland is the haunt of moorland sheep and the Red Grouse. This is a heathland created by man and maintained so by grazing and burning. The Moorland tracts are dominated by relatively few plant species but offer a richer ecosystem than the reseeded fields at the Moorland edge which in the absence of costly fertiliser quickly regress to rank unpalatable grassland characterised by the vigorous growth of Conglomerate Rush *(Juncus conglomeratus)*. In the absence of man's activities we cannot expect natural re-establishment of Sessile Oak-Birch woodland; the natural seed source of the oak is too limited and the moorland soils have become too starved of nutrients to support Oak. However in the absence of burning and grazing, Birch invasion and the establishment of a scattered woodland would continue apace. When a reserve manager has a piece of heathland he must take steps to prevent natural tree colonisation. The heathland is a vegetation held static by man's activities (a biotic climax) and in the absence of man it will move inexorably towards woodland (the climatic climax). If woodland were re-established, open site species would disappear, hence reducing species diversity. Thus in this instance the reserve manager must plan a burning regime which will maintain his heathland. When heathland is adjacent to Forestry Commission land this may not be a viable proposition and an alternative measure is to cut the heather and tree seedlings by hand. No imagination is needed to realise how difficult and labour intensive this management technique is!

The limestone grassland is also a biotic climax, held as grassland by grazing. With the drop in rabbit populations following myxomatosis in the early 1950's scrub invasion into grassland has become a difficult problem. The most charactertistic and beautiful limestone grassland flowers are those intolerant of shade, plants which would disappear in a Hawthorn *(Crataegus monogyna)* scrub. Controlled sheep grazing is the usual partial solution to this problem, but sheep require fencing and this is expensive. Rabbits nibbled the young shoots of the taller grasses and in their absence rank grasses (particularly *Brachypodium sp.*) have spread over large areas. These grasses are unpalatable to sheep and are difficult to eradicate. An alternative to grazing could involve manual removal of shrub and Brachypodium or the more controversial use of selective herbicide treatment.

The acid or alkaline wetland is not a habitat created by man but rather a stage in the natural development of vegetation from open water to the inevitable woodland. This primary succession takes many centuries and progresses much more slowly than the colonisation of heathland or grassland by woody species. This is called secondary succession. The natural and slow drying out of the wetland reserve would not often be considered an immediate management problem, but the activities of man in adjacent areas often include drainage works or peat cutting. Then the reserve manager may be faced with rapid deterioration of his wetland habitat. This century drainage schemes have become increasingly sophisticated and efficient. When a small wetland reserve is surrounded by drained farmland the maintenance of a high water table is the most difficult problem a reserve manager can face. Where a high water table in a marsh is flowing in from a running stream the waterlogged ground is too wet for trees, apart from the odd Willow *(Salix sp.)* and the marsh is in balance with climate and soil conditions. This type of habitat may not need manipulative management. Wetland habitats are very susceptible to trampling damage and visitors should be warned of the unwitting damage they may do. However I have been warned off walking over a wet pasture to look for flowers when this same habitat was being puddled underfoot by a herd of cows; a small herd it is true, but the cows were very large. Perhaps they were admitted into the reserve not for their beneficial grazing habits, but more for their intimidating effect on would-be visitors.

The woodland presents a new range of problems for the reserve manager. Almost every woodland tract has been managed by man over many centuries. A primary woodland is one which has existed on a site since the trees returned after the last Ice Age. These small relict woodlands have been managed for coppice crops. This coppice cycle opens up the forest floor to streaming sunshine every twenty or so years and increases the floral diversity of the woodland floor. About 50 years ago this labour intensive practice became uneconomic and in many woodlands only the spring flora has the opportunity to feel the brilliance of the sun's rays. Scrub, Nettle *(Urtica dioica)* and Bramble *(Rubus fruticosus)* are choking small woodland tracts and woodland flowers are disappearing. It is becoming a common strategy for reserve managers to undertake a renewed coppice cycle in order to continue the light and shade cycles that forest plants have become adapted to for over a thousand years.

Our primary woodlands contain many alien species which have been introduced into Britain by man. Horsechestnut *(Aesculus hippocastanum)* was probably brought in by the Romans. This attractive tree is a welcome part of our rural landscape and does not appear to compete with our native trees. In contrast Sycamore *(Acer pseudoplatanus)* is a very aggressive alien which can produce vast quantities of young seedlings which grow quickly and appear supremely adapted to our climate. Sycamore was introduced around 1600 from central Europe and its frequent invasion of primary woodlands creates a problem. Sycamore does not support the rich flora and fauna of micro-organisms, insects and invertebrates that are found in the branches of a native tree.

The alien tree is akin to a ghost town where the branches form a network of streets and the leaves, the houses; but the inhabitants are scarce, the town is deserted. This is in great contrast to the teeming population supported by a native tree. Conservationists often neglect to explain these unfavourable attributes of an alien species. The public then believe that the naturalist is irrational in his hatred of alien trees and think this is an emotional response akin to the Englishman's supposed suspicion of foreigners. Rhododendron *(Rhododendron ponticum)* is another plant which often needs to be controlled in a woodland reserve. All the previous comments apply to this species, but in addition the plant is evergreen casting a perpetual shade and has leathery leaves which decay slowly and then render the soil more acid.

The total area of the Park under tree canopy is increased by the Forestry Commission plantations of conifers. These plantations have all the negative attributes of the Rhododendron, and are planted in dense monoculture. The herbaceous flora in these forests is sparse but in certain areas the woodland rides will have much botanical interest. When these forest tracts are over poor acid moorland soils and are limited in acreage they do offer woodland protection for bird, insect and mammal and an alternative landscape to that of rolling moorland. It is clear that most reserves have to be manipulated by the reserve manager if species diversity and habitat continuity is to be maintained. Looking at each habitat in turn we can see that each distinct environment presents its own special problems. The management objectives, techniques and solutions discussed are not the exclusive preserve of the reserve manager. These comments are relevant to any landowner or occupier who has recognised the value of his wild habitats and seeks to maintain and improve plant and animal life.

Conservation attracts many extremes of opinion. Are we seeking to conserve our natural habitats for man in the 1980's to explore, man in future centuries to enjoy and possibly exploit, or for the wild communities of animals and plants themselves with Homo Sapiens taking the role of custodian rather than co-inhabitor? Some workers in the conservation field believe that habitats should be protected from man and public access strictly limited. In the face of increasing public pressure on the countryside, this view could well gain favour. Purchase of new nature reserves, and maintenance of existing reserves requires massive amounts of public money. Can we expect the working population of the country to give funds to save wild habitats, flowers and animals that they will never be encouraged or allowed to see? As a reserve management committee member I have often felt that the strongest voices in favour of the closed reserve concept come from people in the privileged position of being able to enjoy free access to their own reserve and by a tacit mutual access club to all other reserves. It must be recognised that open access brings the danger of trampling and habitat destruction. The conservationist must walk a tightrope. The public should on the one hand be encouraged to visit and enjoy wild habitats but on the other recognise the dangers of trampling and disturbance to wildlife.

As interest in natural history and conservation increases, people's views on these various subjects are certain to become polarised in the light of their own experience. Strong opinions seem more common than a spirit of compromise.

Is it correct to present these various opinions and then when concluding my discussion, remain impartial without declaring my own position? It is much more honest to state that within the framework of a healthy vigorous habitat I favour a management of minimum interference, and maximum public access. For myself it could not be otherwise. I believe that current knowledge of the dynamics of natural communities is limited and should not encourage over-enthusiastic manipulation of habitats or use of chemical control measures. The future of wildlife conservation in Britain lies in the hands of the public. As more people walk the Moors seeing the flowers on the hillside, the butterflies basking in the sun, hearing the bird song on the wind, and smelling the fragrant wild blossom, the greater will be the chances of the long-term survival of these priceless natural habitats.

ACCESS AND NATURE RESERVES

Fen Bog   Reserve of Yorkshire Wildlife Trust (Y.W.T.) SE857982. 40 acres of wetland with interesting mixture of fen and bog plants. A valley bog with deep peat.

Hagg Wood Marsh   Y.W.T. SE835901. 11 acres of marsh and woodland with good calcareous wetland flora.

Ellerburn Bank   Y.W.T. SE 852847. 7 acres of dry limestone grassland with interesting butterflies and flowers.

Ashberry Pasture   Y.W.T. SE568846. 13 acres of grassland and streamside vegetation.

Hayburn Wyke   Y.W.T. TA 005968. 34 acres of Sessile Oak woodland, much on steep cliff slopes.

Garbutt Wood   Y.W.T. SE506835. 60 acres of mixed woodland and open cliff vegetation, acid and calcareous.

Bridestones   Y.W.T. SE 880904. 625 acres of moorland with a small Sessile Oak woodland.

Little Beck Wood   Y.W.T. NZ879049. 31 acres of woodland.

Visiting permits, further information and membership applications can be obtained from the Yorkshire Wildlife Trust, 10 Toft Green, Micklegate, York.

Forge Valley Woods   National Nature Reserve SE990855 of limestone woodland and riverside vegetation. Good access from public footpaths.

Pickering Forest Trails   Information can be obtained from the Forest Information Centre at Low Dalby.

Ravenscar Geological Trail   NZ980016. Short route 2½ miles; longer route 4½ miles.

Farndale   SE673953. Local Nature Reserve with Daffodil trail.

Cleveland Way   94 mile long distance footpath from Helmsley to Filey.

Mulgrave Woods   Sandsend. Private woods with footpaths which are open to the public in the summer months on Wednesday, Saturday and Sunday.

REFERENCES AND SOURCES FOR FACTS AND FICTION

Aichele, D. 'Wild Flowers, a Field Guide in Colour'. Octopus, 1976.

Arnold, S. M. 'A Simple Field Key to Common British Wild Flowers'. The Author, 1983.

Arnold, S. M. 'Wild Flowers of the Yorkshire Wolds'. Hutton Press, 1985.

Arnold Lees, F. A. 'A Supplement to the Yorkshire Floras'. Ed. C. A. Cheetham and A. W. Sledge. Brown and Sons, 1940.

Baines, H. 'The Flora of Yorkshire'. Longman, Orme, Brown, Green. Longman, 1840.

Baker, J. G. 'North Yorkshire'. Brown and Sons, 1906.

Boyes, M. 'Exploring the North Yorkshire Moors'. A Dalesman Mini Book, 1976.

Cowley, W. 'The Cleveland Way'. A Dalesman Paperback, 3rd ed., 1975.

Culpepper, T. 'Culpepper's Complete Herbal and English Physician'. Facsimile of 1862 ed. Harvey Sales, 1981.

Gordon, L. 'A Country Herbal'. Webb and Bower, 1980.

Mabey, R. 'Food for Free'. Collins, 1972.

Moore, N. W. 'Loss and Damage to S.S.S.I. in 1980'. Nature Conservancy Survey, 1980.

North York Moors National Park Information Service 'Geology of the North York Moors.' 1979.

Paynter, W. H. Ed. 'Primitive Physic'. Parade Printing Works Ltd., Plymouth, 1961.

Raistrick, A. Ed. 'North Yorkshire Moors'. National Park Guide 4. H.M.S.O., 1969.

Reader's Digest 'Field Guide to the Wild Flowers of Britain', 1981.

Richardson, R. 'Hedgerow Cookery'. Penguin Books, 1980.

Sloover, J. and Goossens, M. 'Wild Herbs: a Field Guide'. David and Charles.

Stevens, J. E. 'Discovering Wild Plant Names'. Shire Publications Ltd., 1973.

Summerhayes, V. S. 'Wild Orchids of Britain'. New Naturalist. Collins, 1951.

Wilson, V. 'East Yorkshire and Lincolnshire' (British Regional Geology) H.M. Geological Survey. H.M.S.O., London, 1948.

INDEX

Numbers in **bold** refer to illustrations

95

98

99

100

101

102